Starting SCIENCE
FOR SCOTLAND
BOOK ONE

OXFORD
UNIVERSITY PRESS

OXFORD
UNIVERSITY PRESS

Great Clarendon Street, Oxford OX2 6DP

Oxford University Press is a department of the University of Oxford.
It furthers the University's objective of excellence in research,
scholarship, and education by publishing worldwide in

Oxford New York

Auckland Bangkok Buenos Aires Cape Town Chennai
Dar es Salaam Delhi Hong Kong Istanbul Karachi Kolkata
Kuala Lumpur Madrid Melbourne Mexico City Mumbai Nairobi
São Paulo Shanghai Singapore Taipei Tokyo Toronto

with an associated company in Berlin

Oxford is a registered trade mark of Oxford University Press
in the UK and in certain other countries

© Alan Fraser and David Coppock 2002

The moral rights of the authors have been asserted

Database right Oxford University Press (maker)

First published 2002

British Library Cataloguing in Publication Data

Data available

ISBN 0-19-914833-3

10 9 8 7 6 5 4 3 2 1

Typeset in Stone, Franklin Gothic, and Klepto
by IFA Design, Plymouth UK

Printed in Spain
by Gráficas Estella

Acknowledgements

The authors wish to acknowledge the contributions provided from the
original edition of *Starting Science* by Ian Gilchrist and Tony Partridge.

The publisher would like to thank the following for their kind permission to
reproduce copyright material (SPL = Science Photo Library; OUP = Oxford
University Press):

6 A. G. Johnston/Scotland in Focus; **7** Joseph Sohm;
ChromoSohm Inc./Corbis UK Ltd; **15** Institute of Terrestrial Ecology/SPL; **16tl** A. Fraser/OUP; **16bl** Paul
Brierley; **16tc** A. Fraser/OUP; **16bc** Geoscience Features Picture Library;
16tr Geoscience Features Picture Library; **16br** Geoscience Features Picture
Library; **17** Bernhard Edmaier/SPL; **18** Geoscience Features Picture Library;
19tl Martyn F. Chillmaid; **19bl** Martyn F. Chillmaid; **19tc** Martyn F. Chillmaid;
19tr Tony Craddock/SPL; **19br** Martyn F. Chillmaid; **20t** Geoscience Features
Picture Library; **20b** NASA/SPL; **21tl** Geoscience Features Picture Library;
21tr Mimmo Jodice/Corbis UK Ltd; **21b** Geoscience Features Picture Library;
22tl Geoscience Features Picture Library; **22bl** Sinclair Stammers/SPL;
22tr Simon Fraser/SPL; **22br** Olivier Darmon/Jacana/SPL; **23t** Paul Brierley;
23b Maximilian Stock Ltd/SPL; **24t** A. Fraser/OUP; **24b** Biophoto Associates;

25l Galia, Jerrican/SPL; **25c** Yann Arthus-Bertrand/Corbis UK Ltd; **25r** Richard
Hamilton Smith/Corbis UK Ltd; **26** Martin Bond/SPL; **27tl** Richard Menga/
Fundamental/SPL; **27cl** Sony Manufacturing Company UK; **27bl** Astrid &
Hanns-Frieder Michler/SPL; **27tc** Jerry Mason/SPL; **27cc** Jonathan Watts/SPL;
27bc Martyn F. Chillmaid; **27tr** Martyn F. Chillmaid; **27cr** Freeplay;
27br Charles D. Winters/SPL; **28tl** Martyn F. Chillmaid; **28tr** Addject Ltd;
28b Freeplay; **31** Martin Bond/SPL; **32** Andrew J. G. Bell; Eye Ubiquitous/
Corbis UK Ltd; **33l** Simon Fraser/SPL; **33c** Jet Propulsion Laboratory/NASA;
33r Sheila Terry/SPL; **35** Martin Bond/SPL; **36** Nigel Cattlin/Holt Studios
International; **39** Stone/Getty Images; **40tl** Gallo Images/Corbis UK Ltd;
40cl Bruce Coleman; **40tc** Oxford Scientific Films; **40cc** Adriano Bacchella/
Bruce Coleman; **40tr** HPH Photography/Bruce Coleman; **40cr** Jane Burton/
Bruce Coleman; **40br** Kevin Schafer/Corbis UK Ltd; **42t** OUP; **42c** OUP;
42b OUP; **43t** Biophoto Associates; **43b** Hans Reinhard/Bruce Coleman;
49 OUP; **51** Hulton|Archive; **53t** Volvo Car Corporation; **53bl** BMW Landhut;
53bc Pilkington PLC; **53br** Martin Bond/SPL; **54l** Stone/Getty Images;
54c Catherine Karnow/Corbis UK Ltd; **54r** Martyn F. Chillmaid; **56l** Peter
Gould; **56c** Peter Gould; **56r** Peter Gould; **57l** Geoscience Features Picture
Library; **57r** Martyn F. Chillmaid/SPL; **58l** Peter Gould; **58c** Peter Gould;
58r Tek Image/SPL; **59** OUP; **60** Vince Streano/Corbis UK Ltd; **61tl** Jennie
Woodcock/Corbis UK Ltd; **61tr** Martyn F. Chillmaid; **61b** Newell Ltd; **62** SPL;
66 Scottish Television (STV); **69** Peter Gould; **70** Peter Gould; **71** Martyn F.
Chillmaid; **73** Colin McPherson/Scottish Viewpoint; **74l** Gene Cox;
74r Biophoto Associates; **75t** Nigel Cattlin/Holt Studios International;
75b Iain Sarjeant/Bruce Coleman; **76tl** Dr Tony Brain/SPL; **76bl** Harold
Taylor/Oxford Scientific Films; **76tc** Quest/SPL; **76bc** Eye of Science/SPL;
76tr Gene Cox; **76br** Andrew Syred/SPL; **80** Jerrican Gaillard/SPL; **81** Zooid
Pictures; **82** Gene Cox; **83t** OUP; **83b** Vince Streano/Corbis UK Ltd; **86tl** Bruce
Coleman; **86bl** J. H. Robinson/SPL; **86tc** Bruce Coleman; **86bc** Dr Jeremy
Burgess/SPL; **86tr** Bruce Coleman; **86cr** Claud Nuridsany & Marie
Perennou/SPL; **87** Scottish Viewpoint; **88c** Charles D. Winters/SPL;
88a Geoscience Features Picture Library; **88b** Geoscience Features Picture
Library; **88c** Charles D. Winters/SPL; **88d** Geoscience Features Picture Library;
88e Peter Gould; **88f** Charles D. Winters/SPL; **88g** Astrid & Hanns-Frieder
Michler/SPL; **88h** Charles D. Winters/SPL; **88i** Geoscience Features Picture
Library; **88j** Kaj R. Svensson/SPL; **89tl** Charles D. Winters/SPL; **89cl** Peter
Thorne/SPL; **89bl** Geoscience Features Picture Library; **89tcl** Charles D.
Winters/SPL; **89tcr** Charles D. Winters/SPL; **89tr** Geoscience Features Picture
Library; **89cr** Klaus Guldbrandsen/SPL; **89br** Geoscience Features Picture
Library; **90tl** OUP; **90bl** Geoscience Features Picture Library; **90tc** OUP;
90tr OUP; **90br** Tecmap Corporation; Eric Curry/Corbis UK Ltd; **91tl** OUP;
91tc Charles D. Winters/SPL; **91tr** George Post/SPL; **92t** OUP; **92b** James L.
Amos/Corbis UK Ltd; **95t** Martyn F. Chillmaid; **95c** Adam Hart/SPL;
95b AnthonyBannister; Gallo Images/Corbis UK Ltd; **97t** Martin Bond/SPL;
97bl Baxi Group Fires Division; **97br** Martyn F. Chillmaid; **98t** Sinclair
Stammers/SPL; **98b** Simon Fraser/SPL; **99** Claud Nuridsany & Marie
Perennou/SPL; **100** Martin Bond/SPL; **101** The Image Bank/Getty Images;
102tl Roger Ressmeyer/Corbis UK Ltd; **102cl** H. Rogers/Trip & Art Directors
Photo Library; **102bl** Volker Steger/SPL; **102tc** I. Yates/Trip & Art Directors
Photo Library; **102bc** Martyn F. Chillmaid; **102tr** Michael St. Maur
Sheil/Corbis UK Ltd; **102cr** M Barlow/Trip & Art Directors Photo Library;
102br Martyn F. Chillmaid; **105** Downey /Hulton|Archive; **107** Dr Mitsuo
Ohtsuki/SPL; **109** Steve Kaufman/Corbis UK Ltd; **110** Jisas/Lockheed;
111t Topham Picturepoint; **111cl** Chris Honeywell/OUP; **111cr** Edinburgh
Photographic Library; **111b** Power Plastics Ltd; **113** Keren Su/Corbis UK Ltd;
114 Simon Fraser/SPL; **115** OUP; **116l** Zooid Pictures; **116c** Zooid Pictures;
116r Zooid Pictures; **117** Peter Gould; **118l** Worm's Way; **118c** Mark
Edwards/Still Pictures; **118tr** Nigel Cattlin/Holt Studios International;
118br Rosemary Mayer/Holt Studios International; **119** Mike J Thomas/Frank
Lane Picture Agency; **121t** D. P. Wilson/Frank Lane Picture Agency;
121b P. Morris/Ardea; **122t** Niall Benvie/Corbis UK Ltd; **122b** John
Daniels/Ardea; **124tl** Kathie Atkinson/Oxford Scientific Films; **124bl** Natural
Selections Inc./Bruce Coleman; **124tc** Terry Whittaker/Frank Lane Picture
Agency; **124bc** P. Perry/Frank Lane Picture Agency; **124tr** Bruce Coleman;
124br Hans Reinhard/Bruce Coleman; **125** The Image Bank/Getty Images.

Introduction

Introducing this book...

Your science class is a place for doing experiments. From your previous science lessons you will already know some of the things scientists do. Every day, scientists carry out experiments, trying to find the answers to many different problems. In fact, science is really all about doing experiments.

But your science class is also a place for reading books. Scientists spend lots of time reading books, searching for information, looking up instructions about how to do experiments, finding out what other scientists have done. You need to practise this skill, too.

Starting Science for Scotland students' book has been written to be your course companion while you are studying science in S1 and S2. It has a number of jobs to do. And it has been written especially to help you

➲ to understand what you find out in your own experiments
➲ to develop further your scientific thinking skills
➲ to see more where science fits into everyday life, how important science is, and how much scientists have been able to improve the world we all live in.

...and how to use it

Starting Science for Scotland is made up of units. Most units contain three pages:

➲ **Starting off** is the first page. Here, you will learn a new piece of science. You should begin with this page. Otherwise, the other pages may not make any sense.
➲ **Going further** is the second page. It follows on from what you learned in Starting off.
➲ **For the enthusiast**, the third page, takes you even further. The material here is usually more difficult.

Each unit also begins with a photograph relating in some way to the content of the chapter. This is bonus material to set you thinking in some cases beyond the material in the rest of the course.

When you start to work on a page, you should first read everything **thoroughly – including Did You Know?** You should also look carefully at any diagrams. Then you can answer the questions. Some questions end with a triangle sign (▲). This tells you that the answer to the question is written somewhere on the page. Some questions begin **Try to find out.** You will usually have to look through other books – like encyclopaedias – for the answers to these. To answer the other questions, you will have to use what you have learned on the page and a bit of brain power!

In writing *Starting Science for Scotland*, we have also tried to find things which will interest you and things which you will enjoy doing. We hope that we have succeeded!

Alan Fraser

1 Scientific skills

In 1774, a team of scientists from London set off for Mount Schiehallion, near Kinloch Rannoch. They wanted to answer a big question: what is the strength of gravitation throughout the entire universe? And they had thought of a clever way to find out. Everything that has a mass attracts everything else that has a mass: that's what gravity is. So the scientists set up thin wires with small masses on the ends on either side of the mountain, which they chose because it is very symmetrical, as you can see. They then measured how much these plumb lines were pulled from the vertical towards the mountain (because of the gravitational force between the mountain and the masses on the wires). From this, they were able to calculate a value close to that which today's scientists have determined to high accuracy. (If you ever go to Schiehallion, you can see a plaque there that commemorates this important experiment.) Their investigation required them to plan carefully and safely what they were going to do. They had to measure accurately to obtain reliable data. And they had to link the results of their observations with theory. They used the methods of science, some of which you will now look at in this first chapter.

Scientists have made many, many important and useful discoveries. A few of them have happened by accident. Most of them, however, have been the results of lots of hard work and careful investigation.

> **Learning to investigate is the most important thing in science.**

You can carry out an investigation like this:

Step 1 **Start by asking questions.**

(That's how scientific investigations usually begin.)

Why did my bicycle rust so badly last winter?
How can I stop it from rusting?

Step 2 **Think about all the things which could have an effect. Make a list.**

What could have affected my bicycle?
(Freezing temperatures? Sand on the road? Salt in the sand? Snow?)

Step 3 **Choose one thing to investigate.**

Salt could make a difference!

Step 4 **Set up an experiment to carry out the investigation. Make sure that it is a fair experiment and a safe one. Choose all the equipment and chemicals you need.**

A bicycle is made of steel, which is mostly iron. Find out if an iron nail rusts faster in tap water or salt water.

Step 5 **Do the experiment – observe what happens. Write down your results.**

In this experiment, you will have to wait for quite a while, but then you should see clearly what happens. Writing things down at the time makes sure that you don't forget!

Step 6 **Try to work out what has happened and why.**

Write down your ideas. Discuss them with a friend. Try to find the answer to your question.

Why does the bicycle rust?

Could it be the salt? The cold? The sand?

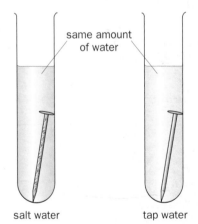
same amount of water

salt water   tap water

What has happened? Why?

QUESTIONS

1 On a page at the back of your exercise book, write down the *six* steps for an investigation. Read them before you start any investigating.

2 What would you do to investigate if rusting is worse when the temperature is low?

3 Write down what you would do to investigate

a if the shape of a piece of plasticine affects whether it sinks or floats

b if things float better in fresh water or sea water.

4 **Try to find out** how you can stop your bicycle from rusting.

A science lab can be a dangerous place. Carelessness can cause accidents. **That's why it is vital that you work safely – for your own sake and for the sake of everyone else in your class.** And that's why it's important to have a set of safety rules.

Use the pictures below to help you to write your own safety rules:

1 Spot seven differences between the two pictures.
2 Write a safety rule about each difference.

Science class AZ (a danger to everyone)

Science class AZ (on their best behaviour)

In many ways, the most important part of an investigation is the beginning. You have to think about what you are trying to find out and plan the experiment carefully if it is going to be successful.

Ron and Stan were asked to do a 'fair test' investigation. They had to do an experiment where they used Bunsen burners to heat water. They had to find out if the yellow flame is hotter than the blue flame.

Stan planned out the experiment. Ron didn't.

The results were very different!

Ron's rush

Ron wanted to be first with the answer. He rushed round the lab, grabbing the first apparatus he could find. He quickly ran water into two beakers (using both taps at the sink to speed things up). Then he lit the gas and started timing. Three minutes later he shouted out, 'The yellow flame's the winner.'

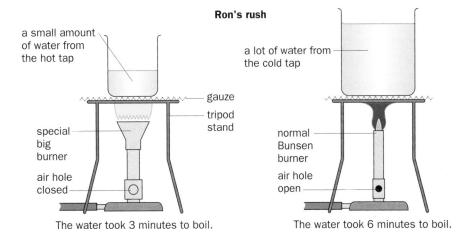

Ron's rush

a small amount of water from the hot tap

a lot of water from the cold tap

gauze
tripod stand

special big burner

normal Bunsen burner

air hole closed

air hole open

The water took 3 minutes to boil.

The water took 6 minutes to boil.

Stan's plan

Stan spent five minutes thinking, 'How can I make a fair test?' Then he searched for the correct apparatus. He set it up carefully, lit the gas, and started timing. His results showed that the blue flame was the hotter.

The teacher didn't agree with Ron. She told him to think again and then repeat the experiment. But she was pleased with Stan. He had worked carefully and found the correct answer.

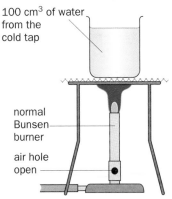

Stan's plan

$100 \, cm^3$ of water from the cold tap

$100 \, cm^3$ of water from the cold tap

normal Bunsen burner

normal Bunsen burner

air hole closed

air hole open

The water took 7 minutes to boil.

The water took 4 minutes to boil.

1 Why did Ron decide that the yellow flame was hotter?
2 How did Stan 'make a fair test'?
3 Suggest *three* reasons why Ron got the wrong answer.
4 The owner of a car hire company wants to compare the distances which a Renault Clio and a Ford Ka can travel on 10 litres of petrol. Plan out a fair test she could use to do this.
5 **Try to find out** how fair tests are carried out to discover
   a which washing powder washes best
   b which battery lasts longest.

The rule for doing fair test experiments

Keep everything about the experiments the same...

...apart from the one thing you are investigating.

When you are doing experiments, you can use your senses to make observations. You can see colours change and gases being given off, and hear 'the pop' of an explosion. But you can't use your senses for everything. You can't use your senses, for example, to find out how long water takes to boil or how hot bath water is. And you can't always rely on your senses. The same air may seem warm to one person and cold to another. It all depends on what they are used to.

Fortunately there are many experiments where you don't have to depend on your senses to make observations. Measuring instruments can be used instead. **Scientists use measuring instruments whenever they can.** You will have already used some – a **stopwatch** (to measure time) and a **ruler** (to measure length) for sure. Below, you can see three other instruments and what they measure.

1 Measuring cylinder

A measuring cylinder is used to measure the volume of a liquid (the space it takes up).

The **cubic centimetre** (**cm³**) is the unit of volume used in science. **Litres** (**l**) and **millilitres** (**ml**) are other units of volume.

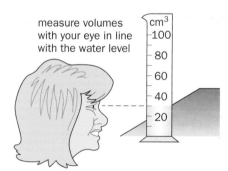

measure volumes with your eye in line with the water level

The measuring cylinder has 30 cm³ of water in it.

2 Thermometer

A thermometer is used to measure the temperature of an object (how hot it is). The unit of temperature is the **degree Celsius** (**°C**).

Human body temperature is 37 °C.

3 Balance

A balance is used to measure the mass of an object (how much material there is in it).

Grams (**g**) and **kilograms** (**kg**) are the units of mass.

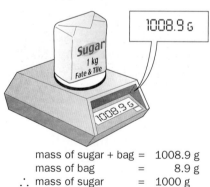

Sugar 1 kg Fate & Tile

1008.9 G

mass of sugar + bag = 1008.9 g
mass of bag = 8.9 g
∴ mass of sugar = 1000 g

The sugar has a mass of 1 kg.

4 What are these (for)?

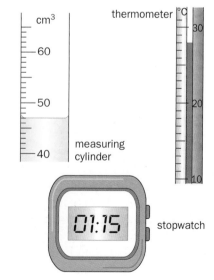

thermometer

measuring cylinder

stopwatch

QUESTIONS

1 What is meant by
   a the volume of a cup of tea
   b the mass of an apple
   c the temperature of the air? ▲
   Which instruments can you use to measure these things? ▲
2 What are the units of
   a temperature?
   b volume?
   c mass?
3 Make a list of *five* measuring instruments used in your home.
4 What are the measurements on the instruments opposite?
5 **Try to find out** what happens when a plane is flying 'on autopilot'.

Tables

Very often, an experiment gives you lots of **data** (scientific information). The data can be very useful – if you organize it well.

Sometimes the data is put in a **table**. That's useful because it collects all the information together. Then you can look at all of the results at the same time and compare them.

May	1	2	3	4	5	6	7
night time temperature (at 11.00 p.m.)	2 °C	0 °C	–1 °C	5 °C	6 °C	7 °C	2 °C
amount of cloud at 11.00 p.m.	☁	☁	none	☁	☁	☁	☁
day time temperature (at 11.00 a.m.)	16 °C	17 °C	18 °C	13 °C	14 °C	13 °C	15 °C
amount of cloud at 11.00 a.m.	☁	☁	none	☁	☁	☁	☁

Some readings from a weather chart

Bar charts

A **bar chart** is useful because it gives a picture of the results. It can let you see at a glance what the results show.

This bar chart shows the heights of the pupils in a science class.

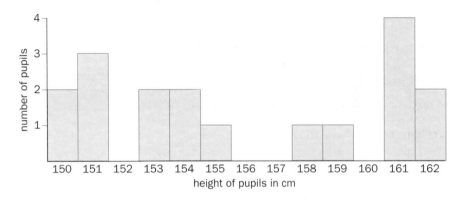

Line graphs

A line graph also gives a picture of your results, but it has an extra advantage. You can use it to read off values which you have not measured.

This graph shows the speed of a racing cyclist at the start of a race. The speed was measured every 5 seconds.

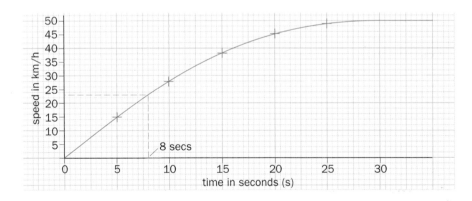

QUESTIONS

1 What are the advantages of putting the data in
  a a table? **b** a bar chart?
  c a line graph?
2 *From the table* write down
  a the highest temperature
  b when the temperature was lowest
  c what effect the amount of cloud had on the temperatures (morning and night).

3 *From the bar chart* write down
  a the smallest height
  b the most common height
  c how many pupils have height 154 cm or less.
4 *From the graph* write down the cycle's speed after
  a 8 s
  b 20 s.
5 **Try to find out** why the graph levels out after 25 s.

DiD YOU KNOW?

➔ The highest temperature ever recorded was 58 °C, in the Libyan desert, in 1922.

Measuring is usually easy – if you have the correct measuring instrument. But some measurements cause problems. They need some thought.

The volume of an odd-shaped object

You can find the volume of a pebble (or any other odd-shaped object) using a measuring cylinder.

First you put some water in the measuring cylinder and measure the volume. Then you drop in the pebble and measure the volume again. The difference in volume is equal to the volume of the object.

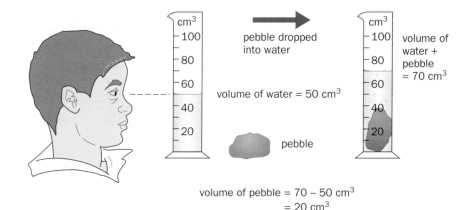

pebble dropped into water

volume of water = 50 cm³

volume of water + pebble = 70 cm³

pebble

volume of pebble = 70 – 50 cm³
= 20 cm³

The time of a pendulum swing

You can make a pendulum from a piece of string and an iron bolt. First you hang the bolt from the string. Then you set the bolt swinging.

No matter how far the bolt swings, the time for one swing is always the same. One swing may be too fast to time accurately. But you can get a good answer by timing several swings.

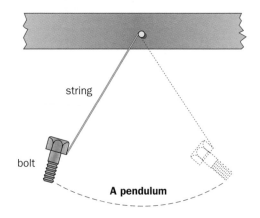

string

bolt

A pendulum

time for 10 swings = 12.0 s

Each swing of the pendulum takes the same time.

$$\therefore \text{ time for 1 swing} = \frac{12.0 \text{ s}}{10}$$

$$= 1.2 \text{ s}$$

The mass of a pin

One pin may not be enough to give a reading on the balance. But there will be a reading with 100 pins on the balance pan.

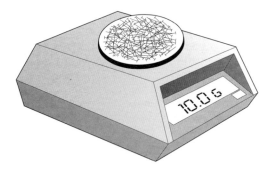

mass of 100 pins = 10.0 g

If all the pins are the same:

$$\text{mass of 1 pin} = \frac{10.0 \text{ g}}{100} = 0.1 \text{ g}$$

If the pins are not exactly the same, 0.1 g is the average mass of 1 pin.

1 a What is special about a pendulum swing? ▲
  b How can you time a pendulum swing accurately? ▲
2 How would you find the mass of a match?
3 Find the average mass of a nail if 50 nails have a mass of 175 g.

4 How would you find the volume of
  a a golf ball? **b** a cork?
5 How long does it take for a midge to beat its wings once?
6 You could find your own volume with a bath of water, a measuring jug, a marker pen, and a bit of help. What would you do?

DiD YOU KNOW?

Scientists have found out that

⮕ a midge insect beats its wings 1000 times each second

⮕ a flu virus is only 0.000 001 5 cm long.

Why are icicles the last thing to melt when there is a thaw?

That's a question three friends were discussing.
They all had different ideas!

⮞ James said that the icicles melted slowly because they hung from the roofs. The friends didn't agree with that!

⮞ They didn't agree with Ashad either. He said that the ice was colder inside an icicle than anywhere else.

⮞ But they did think that Louise might be correct. She thought that small crystals of ice (which make up snow) melt faster than big pieces of ice (like an icicle).

They decided to do an investigation to find out if Louise was correct. They couldn't do it with snow and icicles – it was September! They used ice from the freezer instead. They used ice cubes instead of the icicles and crushed-up ice instead of the snow. Then they tried to find out which melted faster.

In the diagrams you can see the experiment they did...

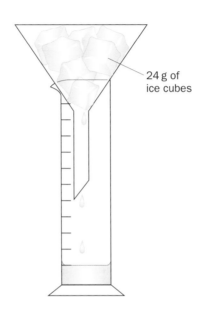

24 g of ice cubes

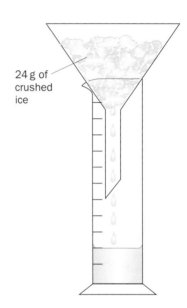

24 g of crushed ice

...and the results they collected.

water collected		water collected
4 cm^3	after 10 minutes	8 cm^3
8 cm^3	after 20 minutes	15 cm^3
11 cm^3	after 30 minutes	22 cm^3
14 cm^3	after 40 minutes	24 cm^3

QUESTIONS

1 What were the friends investigating? How did they try to make it a fair test?

2 How much water had collected from the ice cube after **a** 10 minutes? **b** 20 minutes? How much had collected from the crushed ice?

3 Do you think that Louise was correct? Explain your answer.

4 Ashad said that they should do another experiment. He suggested using 24 g powdered ice from the inside walls of the freezer. Do you think it would have melted faster or slower? Why?

5 Complete this sentence:
The crushed ice melted (faster/slower) than the ice cube. I think that this happened because...

6 **Try to find out** how hailstones are formed.

DID YOU KNOW?

⮞ A hailstone is a lump of ice with lots of layers in it. The biggest ever hailstone was 20 cm across and had a mass of 700 g.

After the experiment...

The three friends sat down after the icicle experiment and tried to work out what their results showed. What had happened? Why?

This time it was Ashad who produced the idea they all liked. He suggested that the crushed ice melted faster because it was spread out more. Spreading out the ice meant that more of it was in contact with the warm air of the room. In the ice cube, however, the warm air could only reach the ice on the outside and couldn't reach most of the ice inside. That's why it melted slowly.

James thought that, if it worked for ice, it might work for other chemicals. He thought that crushing a chemical into a powder would make it work faster. The others agreed that the idea made sense, and so they tested it out in two more experiments.

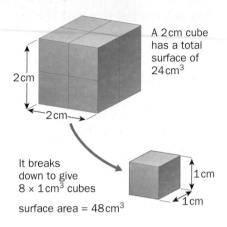

A 2cm cube has a total surface of 24cm³

2 cm
2 cm

It breaks down to give 8 × 1cm³ cubes

surface area = 48cm³

1cm
1cm

Two more experiments

Experiment 1

They took two indigestion tablets and crushed up one. Then they put both into water in beakers and watched to see how quickly gas was given off.

If James' idea were correct, they thought the crushed-up tablet would fizz faster.

Experiment 1

tablet

crushed tablet

fizzing stopped after 2 minutes

fizzing stopped after 30 seconds

Experiment 2

They put a 4 g crystal of sugar and 4 g of crushed-up sugar in water. Then they watched to see how quickly the sugar dissolved.

They thought that if James' idea were correct, the crystal would dissolve more slowly.

Experiment 2

4 g of powdered sugar

4 g sugar crystal

dissolved after 2 hours

still not dissolved after 6 hours

DiD YOU KNOW?

➲ Crushing fuels into powder makes them burn faster and more cleanly. In some power stations, crushed-up coal is used. Surprisingly, it is mixed with water and sprayed into a flame. It gives lots of heat quickly and creates less pollution.

1 Ashad suggested a reason why crushed-up ice melted faster. What was it? ▲
2 What did James suggest? How did his friends test his suggestion? ▲
3 What effect does crushing an indigestion tablet have on the speed at which gas is given off?

Give evidence for your answer.
4 What effect does crushing a sugar lump have on the rate at which it dissolves? Give evidence for your answer.
5 Was James' idea a good one? Explain your answer.

The Earth and its rocks

Now that we can produce images of our home planet from satellites in space, we can see things that it was not possible to see only 50 years ago. For instance, this is a satellite image of the Ardnamurchan peninsular just north of Mull in the west of Scotland. It has been coloured to highlight various features of the landscape: heather-covered moorland is pink, bogs are turquoise, bracken is orange, and grassland is green. But particularly interesting are the rings of colour near the centre, which reveal…a long-extinct volcano! You can even see bare rocks along the rim of the volcano: they are coloured light grey. In this chapter, you will learn more about the melting pots of volcanoes and the rocks that they produce, as well as other types of rocks.

This is what the Earth looks like inside. At least that's what geologists believe. **Geologists** are scientists who study rocks. They think that the Earth is made up of three main layers – the **core**, the **mantle**, and the **crust**. In the picture, you can see what these different layers are like.

The crust is the part that is most important to us. It's the part we live on! Much (71%) of it is covered by sea. The rest of it is land which is covered with rocks, stones, soil and sand. There are hundreds of different types of rock. Here are six commonly found in Britain.

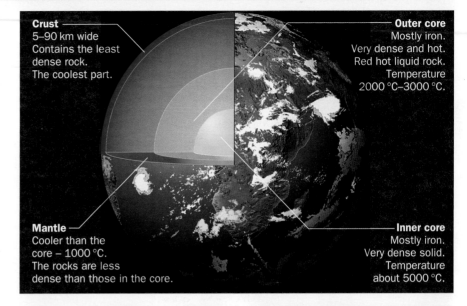

Crust
5–90 km wide
Contains the least dense rock.
The coolest part.

Outer core
Mostly iron.
Very dense and hot.
Red hot liquid rock.
Temperature 2000 °C–3000 °C.

Mantle
Cooler than the core – 1000 °C.
The rocks are less dense than those in the core.

Inner core
Mostly iron.
Very dense solid.
Temperature about 5000 °C.

Granite
Very hard rock – not easily scratched – contains big crystals which make it sparkle – does not react with acid

Sandstone
Softer rock – made of grains of sand which can be rubbed off with your nail – does not react with acid

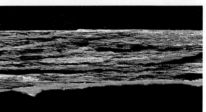

Slate
Rock with crystals – hard but not as hard as granite – made up of flat layers which can be split off – does not react with acid

Basalt
Very hard rock – difficult to scratch – made up of crystals, but the crystals are tiny – does not react with acid

Chalk
Soft rock – made up of tiny white grains which come off if you rub them – fizzes in acid

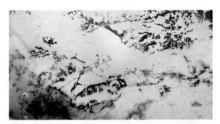

Marble
Rock with shiny surface – contains small crystals – hard but can be scratched with a knife – fizzes in acid

1 Describe what the Earth is like inside. ▲
2 What is the crust like? What is it covered with? ▲
3 Sort the rocks on this page into sets of
  a very hard rocks
  b rocks with crystals
  c rocks with grains. ▲

4 Which rocks do you think are most like each other? Why?
5 Which will last longer, granite or sandstone steps? Why?
6 Why is chalk used for writing?
7 **Try to find out** what slate is used for.

DiD YOU KNOW?
➲ The Earth's core is almost as hot as the Sun.
➲ Granite is so hard that diamond-tipped saws have to be used to cut it. Diamond is the hardest substance found in nature!

Granite is one of a large number of rocks which have crystals in them. These crystals give a clue about how the rocks were formed.

Crystals of a solid can be made by
1 *heating the solid until it melts to a liquid*, and then
2 *allowing the hot liquid to cool until it forms a solid again.*

Geologists believe that the crystals in granite, and in many other rocks, were made by the cooling of hot liquid rock called **magma**. Magma is formed under the Earth's surface in places where there is enough heat to melt the rock. Sometimes the molten rock pushes its way upwards. If it cools enough to solidify, it produces rocks with crystals in them. The slower the cooling, the bigger the crystals are.

Rock which is formed when hot liquid rock cools and hardens is called **igneous rock**. The diagram shows how different kinds of igneous rock can form.

Molten flowing lava

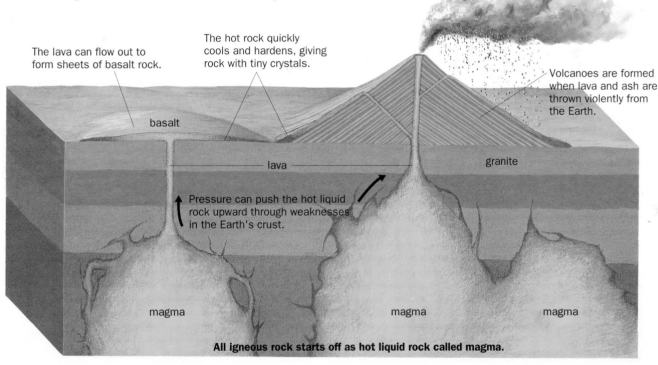

The lava can flow out to form sheets of basalt rock.

The hot rock quickly cools and hardens, giving rock with tiny crystals.

Volcanoes are formed when lava and ash are thrown violently from the Earth.

basalt

granite

lava

Pressure can push the hot liquid rock upward through weaknesses in the Earth's crust.

magma   magma   magma

All igneous rock starts off as hot liquid rock called magma.

1 What is
   a igneous rock?
   b magma?
   c lava? ▲
2 Explain how the following are formed:
   a magma
   b a volcano. ▲
3 a Why are granite and basalt called igneous rocks? ▲
   b Look up the descriptions of granite and basalt.

Write down what these rocks (and other igneous rocks) have in common.
4 a How does the speed of cooling affect the size of the crystals in a rock? ▲
   b Why are granite crystals much larger than the crystals in basalt?
5 Try to find out what pumice stone is, how it was formed, and why it has holes in it.

DID YOU KNOW?
➲ Volcanic eruptions can be explosive. In 1883, an Indonesian volcano – Krakatoa – blew rocks 50 km into the air.
➲ The largest volcano in the Solar System is on Mars.

No one has ever bored through the Earth's crust. No one was around when the Earth's rocks were being formed. So how can geologists tell what was going on? They look for evidence and use it to make the best theories they can.

Evidence from underground

Evidence about the inside of the Earth comes from **seismology** – the study of earthquakes. An earthquake is produced when rocks inside the Earth suddenly slip. This sets up huge vibrations called **seismic waves**. The waves travel through different rocks at different speeds. By measuring the speeds of the underground waves, geologists can build up pictures of what the inside of the Earth is like.

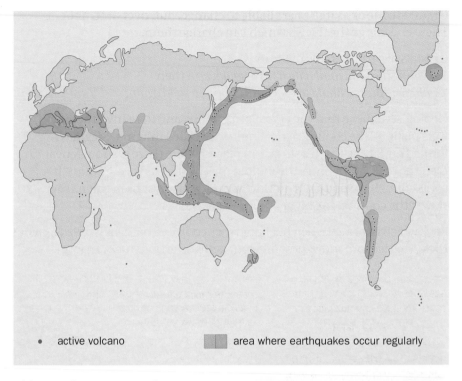

• active volcano   ▨ area where earthquakes occur regularly

Studies like this have shown that the Earth's crust has many weaknesses called **faults**. Earthquakes often happen along faults. Molten rock can also force its way up faults. This could lead to the formation of new volcanoes.

Evidence from the surface

There are lots of pieces of evidence from the rocks on the surface. The size of the crystals in an igneous rock, for example, gives evidence of where the rocks were formed.

If an igneous rock has small crystals, it is likely to have been made on or near the surface, where the rock can cool down fast. A rock with large crystals would have been formed deep underground where cooling was slow. If a rock with large crystals is found on the surface, the rock could have been thrown up by big earth movements. Another possibility is that, over many years, softer rock above it was worn away.

Diamonds – large crystals formed when molten rock cools slowly deep underground: they look very 'rough' when they come out of the ground but can then be cut and polished for jewellery.

1 How is an earthquake produced? ▲
2 What is
   a seismology?
   b a seismic wave? ▲
3 Why do geologists find it useful to study seismic waves? ▲
4 What is a fault? Why are volcanoes produced at faults? ▲
5 Using the map, name some countries which are badly affected by earthquakes and volcanoes.
6 **Try to find out** what obsidian is and how it was formed.
7 **Try to find out** as much as you can about King Arthur's Seat.

DiD YOU KNOW?

⊃ The effects of an earthquake can travel a long way. In 1994, a quake in Peru was felt by many Americans – 10 000 km away.

⊃ The deepest ever hole drilled was 12 km deep. But it was still a long way from reaching the mantle.

Rocks don't look as if they are liable to change, but, over time, they do. Here are some of the things which can change them.

1 Heating and cooling

Roasting a small piece of granite and cooling it by dropping it into water breaks off small pieces.

In nature, the temperature changes are not nearly so great, but hot sunny days and freezing cold nights can break tiny pieces off rocks.

2 Freezing water

Air was squeezed out of two lumps of clay, then one was put in a freezer overnight. When the water froze, it split up the clay. (Water produces a great force when if freezes.)

In nature, this can happen when water freezes in cracks in rocks.

3 Friction

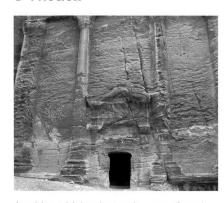

Anything which rubs against a soft rock can rub off grains. Even strong winds can!

If strong winds create a sandstorm, the effect is greater. The wind blows the sand on to the rock and rubs it away. That's what wears away rocks in a desert area where sandstorms are quite common.

4 Pressure

Pressure can change rocks also, particularly if there are high temperatures. It's not possible to show this with rocks, but layers of plasticine can give you an idea of what happens. Pressing on the layers can make them twist and buckle. This can happen to layers of rock deep underground where pressures and temperatures are high.

DID YOU KNOW?
➲ Sandblasting is used to clean up buildings. When jets of tiny grains of sand are fired at the stone, the dirty surface is worn away, leaving the clean stone underneath.

1 Name *four* things which can change rocks.
2 Freezing water can crack rocks. Explain how.
3 Friction can also change rocks. Explain how.
4 What do sandstorms in the desert and sandblasting have in common?
5 Give a clue which can help you to decide that a rock had been changed by pressure.
6 **Try to find out** other things which can be damaged by freezing water.

Mountains don't last for ever, even if they are made of granite! The rocks are attacked by all types of weather.

⊃ Wind, rain, and snow beat down on the rock surface.

⊃ Water seeps into cracks in the rock and then freezes.

⊃ As the water turns to ice, it expands, cracking the rock.

⊃ Hot sunshine followed by cold nights makes rocks expand and then contract. It also makes rocks crack.

All of this makes rock break up. This is called **weathering**. The broken bits of rock can vary in size from large pebbles down to small grains of sand, and even tinier grains of mud or clay. The rock fragments are carried off by wind and/or water. This is called **transport**. During transport, rock fragments are bashed against each other. This whole process is called **erosion**. New rocks can be made from the bits of rock. This is what happens:

Glaciers grind down rocks. This river, running from a glacier, is white with rock fragments.

3 The river water slows down as it reaches the sea. There, the sand, gravel, and pebbles settle as sediment on the sea bed.

1 Weathering breaks down the rocks. The rock fragments are carried off by the wind or washed into streams and rivers.

2 The rivers carry the bits of rock down to the sea (or into a lake). Fast rivers can carry down bigger pebbles than slow ones.

4 Layers of sediment pile up. If this happens over a long period of time, the sediment at the bottom of the pile is squashed. A kind of cement is produced, which sticks the grains together. A new rock, called **sedimentary rock**, is produced.

Sandstone was made in this way from small grains of sand.
Mudstone, **shale**, and **clay** were made from even smaller grains.
Limestone and **chalk** are also sedimentary rocks, but the sediment which made them was rather unusual.
They were made from the shells and skeletons of tiny prehistoric sea animals, which died, fell to the sea bed, and were buried and squashed.

Sediment at the mouth of a river

1 What happens when
 a weathering affects a rock?
 b erosion affects a mountain? ▲

2 Describe how bits of rock from a mountain can get into the sea. ▲

3 What is sediment made of? How is sedimentary rock made? ▲

4 Limestone is a sedimentary rock. Suggest how it was formed.

5 Why is river sand rougher than beach sand? ▲

6 Read about sedimentary rocks elsewhere in this book, then write down things which sedimentary rocks have in common.

7 A large lorry can carry 10 tonnes. How many lorries could be filled by the sediment carried down by the Mississippi in one day?

DiD YOU KNOW?

⊃ The Mississippi river carries over 500 million tonnes of sediment to the sea each year.

⊃ Grains and pebbles are worn smooth as the water carries them along. That's why beach sand, which is always on the move, is smoother than river sand.

Many statues are made of marble. It is a hard, attractive rock made of crystals which sparkle in the light. You wouldn't use limestone for a statue. It is made of grains which are easily scratched off and is not at all shiny.

Marble and limestone seem to be very different, but they both 'fizz' when dropped into acid. That's because they are made of the same mineral – **calcite**.

Marble is a **metamorphic rock**, a rock which has been made by changing another one.

The diagram shows one way in which marble could have been made from limestone. Hot magma has pushed its way upwards into beds of sedimentary rock. As the molten rock cooled and solidified, lots of heat was given out. This heat baked the rock next to it. The calcite grains were changed into calcite crystals, changing the limestone into marble.

High pressures can also change rocks. Some **slate**, for example, was made when mudstone was squashed deep underground. Under pressure, the tiny mudstone grains were changed into flat crystals. These crystals grew along layers. That's why slate can be split easily.

From this, a piece of limestone…

…**to this**, a marble statue

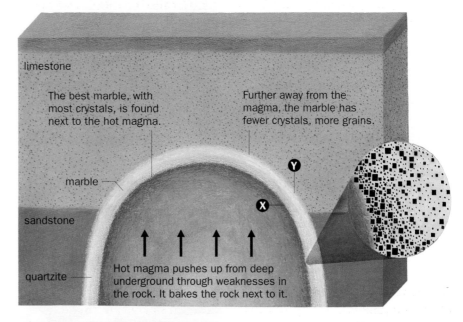

limestone

The best marble, with most crystals, is found next to the hot magma.

Further away from the magma, the marble has fewer crystals, more grains.

marble

Y

X

sandstone

quartzite

Hot magma pushes up from deep underground through weaknesses in the rock. It bakes the rock next to it.

DID YOU KNOW?

➲ Underground, pressures are huge: 10 km down, rocks are affected by a pressure of 20 tonnes on each square centimetre of rock.

➲ Marble statues which stand outside are often covered over during winter to prevent them from being attacked by acid rain.

Heat and pressure, working together, can bend and twist rocks. These metamorphic rocks are found in Devon.

QUESTIONS

1 What is a metamorphic rock? Name *two* different examples. ▲
2 Why do marble and limestone both fizz in acid? ▲
3 Explain how limestone can be changed into marble. ▲
4 Explain how slate can be formed. ▲
5 In the diagram, the marble at X is mostly made of crystals. The marble at Y has crystals and grains. Why is there a difference?
6 **Try to find out** what else marble has been used for.

Underwater?

Are you living on land which was once under water? You may be able to answer this question for yourself – if you investigate the rocks in your area. The rocks may hold the clues you need.

The rocks may clearly show grains of sand, or gravel or pebbles. In that case you can be fairly certain that you are standing on land which was formed under water, from sediment.

The rocks may be made up of layers. This is also good evidence that they were formed under water. When sediment settles out on the bed of a lake or sea, it forms layers. When the sediment is squashed into rock, the rock is also formed in layers.

Rocks may contain fossils

Fossils are traces of prehistoric life. Most were formed from the remains of animals or plants which were buried in the sediment. Sometimes parts of the animal or plant were preserved. More often, a 'print' of the animal or plant was left. The parts of the animal were replaced by chemicals which filled the same shape.

The type of fossil found in an area gives information about the area's history. Your local rocks may, for example, contain fossils of corals, animals that live in shallow seas. If the rocks do have coral fossils, you are probably living on a prehistoric sea bed.

A rock made of sand, gravel, and pebbles

Rock in layers: the Grand Canyon, USA

Coral fossils

A dinosaur footprint

1 Write down *three* clues which might tell you that a rock was formed under water. ▲
2 Why is sedimentary rock often made up of layers? ▲
3 What is a fossil? How were fossils formed? ▲
4 A quarry has lots of coral fossils. What does this tell you about the rock in the quarry? Explain your answer.
5 Try to explain why igneous rocks don't have fossils in them.
6 **Try to find out** if any fossils have been found near your town.

All around you

For thousands of years, humans built homes with stone from local quarries. In Aberdeen, for example, granite was used. In Gloucester, many houses were built from limestone, and in York, they were built from sandstone. Slate was the most widely used stone of all. It is particularly useful because it can be split into thin sheets which can be used on roofs. But now, stone isn't used much. It's too expensive.

Manufactured building materials

Nowadays, one rock – **clay** – is used for building more than any other. On its own, clay is not at all useful. Dry clay is a brittle, weak sedimentary rock made of tiny grains. When it is wet, it gets soft.

But clay is useful because wet clay can be moulded into different shapes. **Firing** the clay in huge ovens called **kilns** turns it into a very hard substance. Clay is used to make many building materials, such as bricks, roof tiles, and chimney pots. It is also used to make **cement**, which makes **concrete**.

Stone	Good points	Not so good points
granite	very hard – not affected by pollution – shiny surface - lets water run off	so hard that it is very difficult to cut and shape
sandstone	not so hard – can be cut and shaped easily	does not stand up well to wind, rain, or pollution – lets water soak in
limestone	soft, easily shaped – slightly acid rain keeps it clean by dissolving the surface a little	rain with lots of acid in it eats away the limestone – lets water soak in
slate	hard, strong – not affected by pollution – can be split into sheets – lets water run off	thin sheets are brittle and crack easily

Making bricks

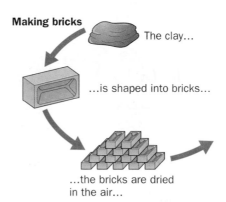

The clay…

…is shaped into bricks…

…the bricks are dried in the air…

…and then fired in a kiln.

Making cement

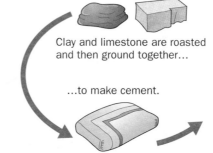

Clay and limestone are roasted and then ground together…

…to make cement.

Mixing the cement with sand, gravel, and water makes concrete.

QUESTIONS

1 Which of the building stones in the table are
   a easy to shape?
   b not affected by pollution? ▲
2 Acid rain can improve or spoil a limestone building. Explain why.
3 Why is natural clay not suitable for building? Describe *two* ways in which it can be made into useful building materials. ▲

4 What is meant by
   a firing clay?
   b a kiln? ▲
5 What advantage does clay have over other rocks used for building?
6 **Try to find out** which stone was used for building in your town? Where did it come from?

DID YOU KNOW?

➔ Bricks have been used for building for over 6000 years. There were no kilns in the earliest days. The bricks were dried by the Sun.

➔ Rocks which let water seep in are said to be **permeable**.

23

All of the time, rocks are being very slowly worn away – by rain, Sun, wind, and frost. In places where there is a glacier, the rocks underneath the glacier are ground down more quickly by the huge mass of moving ice above it. These processes produce tiny grains of rock. The grains make up much of soil.

But soil contains other things, too:

1 Soil contains water

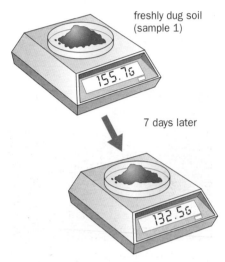

freshly dug soil (sample 1)

155.7g

7 days later

132.5g

When freshly dug soil is left in a dry place, it slowly loses mass. The moisture in it slowly evaporates. Soil moisture is important. Plants need a constant supply of water, which they get through their roots.

2 Soil contains air

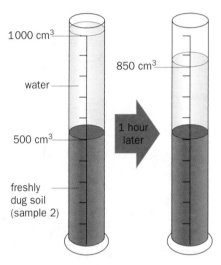

1000 cm^3

water

850 cm^3

500 cm^3

1 hour later

freshly dug soil (sample 2)

When soil is covered with water, the water level slowly drops. The water soaks into the soil as the trapped air escapes. This air in soil is important, too. Oxygen is needed by the roots of plants and by soil animals.

3 Soil contains humus

Humus is mostly made up of material from dead animals and plants which slowly rot away. It helps to keep the soil in good condition in different ways. For one thing, it breaks down to give useful **minerals**, chemicals which plants can use as food.

4 Soil has millions of living organisms in it

Soil is not dead. It's alive with all sorts of organisms. Bacteria and fungi do a really important job: they break down plant and animal material, producing useful minerals which plants need to grow. There are also millions of microscopic worms, and bigger animals such as earthworms, beetles, and moles.

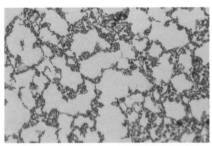

Soil contains millions of tiny animals and other organisms, such as these bacteria.

DID YOU KNOW?

➲ The roots of plants – and even fungi – can break down rocks.

➲ It would take 500 years to make enough soil to cover the Earth's dry land with 2 cm of new soil.

1 Soil is produced from rocks. Explain how. ▲

2 What is humus? Why is it important? ▲

3 What kinds of organisms live in the soil? ▲

4 Why are the following important:
   a soil moisture?
   b soil air? ▲

5 Work out
   a the mass of water in soil sample 1

b the volume of air in soil sample 2.

6 **Try to find out** more about glaciers and soil formation.

Soils from different areas can be very different

Some soils are made up of lots of tiny grains stuck closely together. These are **clay soils**. Clay soils have few air spaces and have water trapped between the grains. As a result, the soils are heavy and drain badly.

Sandy soils are made up of bigger grains with bigger spaces between them. Water can easily pass through these spaces, and so sandy soils are light and easily drained.

The best soils contain some clay, some sand, and lots of humus. A soil like this is called a **loam**. Much of Britain's soil does contain a mixture like this and so is good for farming. The soil in a desert, however, has so much sand that crops don't grow.

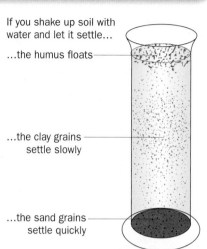

If you shake up soil with water and let it settle...

...the humus floats

...the clay grains settle slowly

...the sand grains settle quickly

Keeping soil 'healthy'

First, farmers have to make sure that they don't lose the soil! That can be a problem on steep mountainsides. In torrential rain, flooding can wash the soil off the slopes very quickly.

Where this is a problem, farmers build terraces on the hillside. These help to hold back the soil.

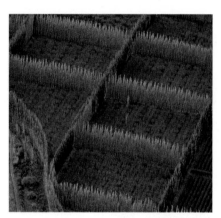

Wind can also be a problem. In the 'dust bowls' of the world, strong winds can blow away huge amounts of soil.

Farmers in such regions protect their soil by growing belts of trees to break the wind's force. They also try to keep crops growing for most of the time. The plant roots keep the soil together.

No matter the type of soil, plants take minerals from it when they grow. These have to be replaced.

In rich countries, this can be done by adding fertilizer, but poorer countries can't afford it. Animal manure and plant compost have to be used instead, but they are in short supply.

QUESTIONS

1 What are the following like:
   a clay soils?
   b sandy soils?
   How can you tell what a soil is made up of?
2 What is
   a humus?
   b a loam?
3 Water and soil can both cause soil to be lost. Explain how, and explain what can be done to prevent the soil loss.
4 Why is it a good idea to plant grass where soil loss because of wind is a problem?
5 **Try to find out** why cutting down trees on mountain slopes can cause soil loss.

DID YOU KNOW?

➲ In the USA, soil is being lost 18 times faster than it is being made. In China, soil loss is 50 times faster.

➲ The soil from a peat bog is almost 100% humus.

Essential energy

Energy can be neither created nor destroyed. In general, it is converted from one form to another. That is the principle of all electricity generating stations. This one is a wave-driven generator on Islay called Limpet. It produces 500 kW of electrical power. More usually they are fuelled by gas or coal. But these can have harmful effects on the environment. What effect do you think this one has on the environment? What would it be like if there were a hydroelectric, coal-burning, or nuclear electricity generating station here instead? How much power could they produce compared to Limpet? In this chapter, you will learn about different forms of energy and our planet's energy resources, as well as more about generating electricity.

These illustrations all show energy changes or conversions taking place.

electrical energy ⟶
light (and heat) energy

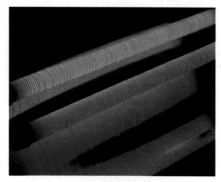

electrical energy ⟶
heat (and light) energy

light energy ⟶ electrical energy

electrical energy ⟶
sound (and heat) energy

moving energy ⟶ sound energy

moving energy ⟶
light (and heat) energy

stored (as chemicals) energy ⟶
heat (and light) energy

stored (as chemicals) energy ⟶
heat (and light) energy

stored (as chemicals) energy ⟶
electrical (and heat) energy

1 List all the different varieties of energy given in the examples above. ▲

2 What is the most common variety of energy that the changes produce? ▲

3 In most of the examples above, some of the energy changed is changed into a form that's not needed. For each one of these write down the energy form not needed. ▲

4 Where does the energy come from to start each of these devices?

5 Identify one other energy conversion and list the energy change(s).

6 **Try to find out** the other names given to
a stored energy
b moving energy.

1 Wind-up toys

These kinds of toys have been around for over a hundred years. There are many different varieties. Some are very complicated and some are very simple. They all work by storing energy and then releasing it.

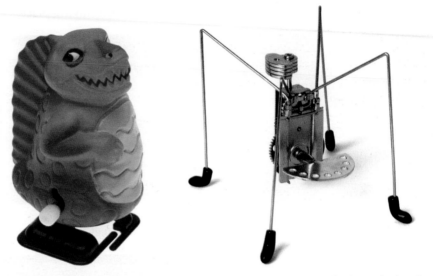

Moving energy (winding up the toy) is converted into stored energy (in the spring) and then released again into moving energy when the toy moves.

2 The wind-up radio

Trevor Bayliss invented the wind-up radio in 1994. To use it, you turn a handle which winds up a large coiled spring inside. When you stop winding and let go, the spring very slowly unwinds. Through a series of gears, it drives a dynamo that powers the radio or, as in the model shown here, charges a rechargeable battery that then powers the radio. This invention has provided people all over the world, often in remote places where no supply of electricity is available, with a source of information they would otherwise not have had.

Moving energy (turning the handle) is converted into stored energy (coiled-up spring). When the handle is released, the stored energy is converted into moving energy again (spring unwinding), then electrical energy (in the turning dynamo), and then stored (chemical) energy in the battery. When the radio is switched on, the stored energy is released in the form of electrical energy, which in turn becomes sound energy (plus some heat).

1 Who invented the wind-up radio? When? ▲
2 What kind of energy is put into the radio? ▲
3 What kind of energy is this changed into? ▲
4 What are the *two* kinds of energy released when the radio is turned on?
5 Where would the wind-up radio prove especially useful?
6 What kind of impact might this radio have on remote communities?
7 Toys like the ones above use stored energy – what other devices can you think of use this form of energy and perform useful tasks?

Energy sketches

When energy changes take place, you can draw a sketch called a **Sankey diagram** to show what changes are taking place. It looks just like a set of arrows. You can draw Sankey diagrams for any device.

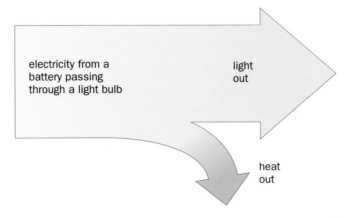

electricity from a battery passing through a light bulb

light out

heat out

This Sankey diagram shows that electricity is changed into light and heat. The width of the arrows give an idea of the amount of energy. In this example, the heat energy is wasted energy, as light is the energy wanted.

Changes in an electric circuit

The circuit on the right shows a selection of components in a series circuit. Sankey diagrams have been drawn for some of the devices when the switch is closed.

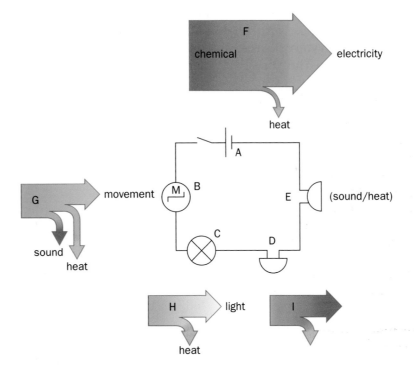

1 Identify the circuit components A, B, C, D, and E.
2 For each component, what are the energy changes shown in the Sankey diagrams F, G, H, and I? ▲
3 Draw the Sankey diagram for component E.

You have named several 'different' types of energy, and so you might think there are a large number of varieties. But most energy is one of two sorts: **kinetic energy** or **potential energy**.

Kinetic energy (KE) is easy to spot

This is probably the easiest energy variety to identify: if something moves, then it has kinetic energy (KE). 'Kinetic' means moving.

Potential energy (PE) is not so easily identified

'Potential' energy means stored energy. You have identified stored energy before. The most obvious stored energies are the fuels: coal, gas, petrol, etc. There are a large number of fuels that readily burn, producing heat.

A battery is a store of chemicals that produce electricity when a circuit is connected to the battery terminals. A battery has PE.

Normally heat energy is given out as part of a process. When chemicals burn (say wood in a bonfire), then heat energy is given out and lost to the surroundings. But suppose you had a hot-water bottle to keep you warm in the night-time. Then you would be using a store of energy – in this case you could refer to the stored heat energy as potential energy.

One of the most important examples of potential energy is the store of energy because of position. *Anything* that has position has potential energy. Water behind a dam wall has potential energy. The block of wood shown on the right has potential energy. In fact, it has two portions of potential energy: one because of its position (it can do something useful on its way down); the other because the chemicals that make up the wood can be burned to produce heat.

The different forms of potential energy are identified by adding a label such as 'chemical' or 'gravitational'.

A fuel has **chemical potential energy**.

Anything high up has **gravitational potential energy**.

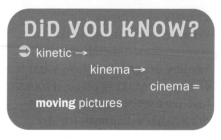

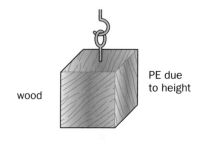

wood — PE due to height

and if it burns, PE due to chemicals

1 Name *three* types of potential energy that are fuels. ▲
2 Why is the cinema so called? ▲
3 Name *three* more types of potential energy (fuels).
4 Why is electricity *not* a form of potential energy.
5 Name a source of energy made from chemicals but *not* a fuel.

Most of the world's energy comes from five main sources. The pie chart opposite shows how much energy comes from each source.

Electricity is *not* included because **all electrical energy is produced from other sources of energy.**

Some electricity – **hydroelectricity** – is produced from the stored energy of water held back by a dam. The water runs downhill from the dam, through a pipeline, to the power station. There it turns huge motors called **water turbines.** The turbines turn generators, and the generators produce electricity. Scotland produces large amounts of hydroelectricity.

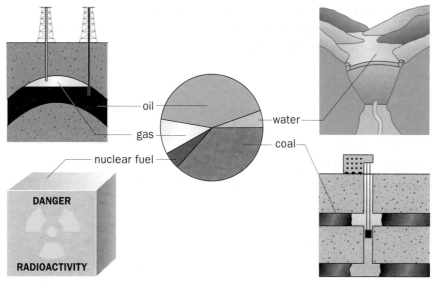

Where the world's energy comes from

Sloy hydroelectric power station on the banks of Loch Lomond produces 130 MW of electricity.

Most countries, however, make their electricity using the chemical energy stored in coal, oil, and gas and the nuclear energy in uranium. The fuels are used to heat water in huge boilers, producing steam. This steam is used to turn **steam turbines**, and these turn the generators.

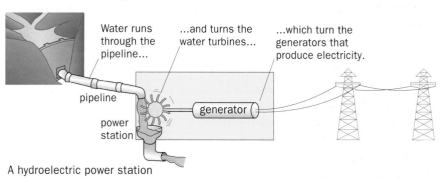

A hydroelectric power station

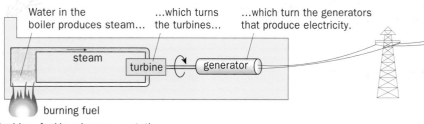

Inside a fuel-burning power station

DiD YOU KNOW?
⮑ 1 kilogramme of uranium can produce as much energy as 60 tonnes of coal.

1 Use the pie chart to name
   a the world's five main energy sources ▲
   b the source which supplies most energy. ▲
2 Why is electricity not called an energy source? ▲
3 How is coal used to make electricity? List the energy changes. ▲
4 **a** Give the energy changes when hydroelectricity is made.
   b Will the energy source for hydroelectricity ever run out? Explain.
5 **Try to find out**
   a the name of your nearest power station and the source of energy it uses
   b why Norway can produce so much hydroelectricity.

31

After electrical energy has been generated at the power station, it has to be **transmitted** (moved from one place to another). There's much more to this than just connecting up the power station and each user by a very long cable!

Of course, cables are involved. The electrical energy is transmitted round the country using thick aluminium or copper cables which are hung from pylons or buried underground. The cables are made of aluminium and copper because these metals are such good conductors. The cables are thick to give low resistance.

Transformers also have a vital part to play. Their job is to change the voltage of the electricity. This has to be done for two main reasons.

1 **Electrical energy is transmitted more efficiently at high voltages.**
Whenever a current flows through a wire, some electrical energy is converted to heat energy. If the electrical energy is transmitted at a high voltage, the current which flows will be small. Then only a small amount of the energy will be wasted as heat. That's why very high voltages are used when electrical energy has to be transmitted over long distances.

2 **Different users require electricity at different voltages.**
Electrical energy is supplied to your home at 230 V, but factories may need an 11 000 V supply, and electrified railways, 25 000 V.

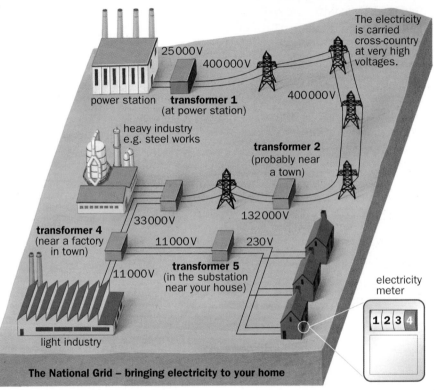

25 000 V
400 000 V
power station   **transformer 1** (at power station)
The electricity is carried cross-country at very high voltages.
400 000 V
heavy industry e.g. steel works
transformer 2 (probably near a town)
132 000 V
transformer 4 (near a factory in town)
33 000 V
11 000 V
transformer 5 (in the substation near your house)
230 V
11 000 V
light industry
electricity meter

| 1 | 2 | 3 | 4 |

The National Grid – bringing electricity to your home

The network which carries electrical energy round the country is called the **National Grid**. It uses **step-up** transformers to increase the voltage, and **step-down** transformers to decrease it.

1 What is meant by transmitted electrical energy? ▲
2 What are transmission cables made of, and why? ▲
3 What is a transformer's job? What is the difference between a step-up transformer and a step-down one? ▲
4 Which of transformers 1–5 in the diagram are step-up and which are step-down? ▲
5 Why is electrical energy supplied at a high voltage? ▲
6 a What is the National Grid?
b Where in the Grid is the voltage highest, and why?
7 **Try to find out** where your nearest substation is.

DID YOU KNOW?

➲ The Grid system must be able to supply extra electricity at some times of the day (like 5 pm, when everyone makes tea!).

➲ There are some power stations which are kept working at half capacity so that they can supply this extra electricity.

The production of energy is not risk-free. Whatever form of production is used, there is always an argument against it.

Energy inefficiency

And you might think energy production is efficient – it isn't. It's very inefficient. Look at the energy flow through a typical power station supplying electricity to the National Grid.

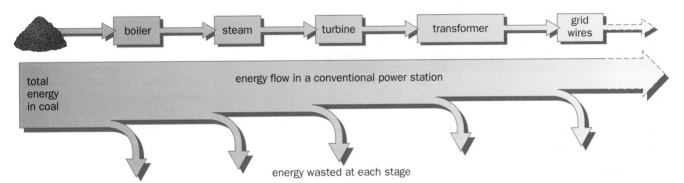

total energy in coal

boiler → steam → turbine → transformer → grid wires

energy flow in a conventional power station

energy wasted at each stage

Other disadvantages

There are many other disadvantages besides the inefficient process of production. Burning fossil fuels produces acid rain and carbon dioxide. Power station cooling water, which is warmed during the process, is often dumped into a local river, or the sea. Increased water temperatures can cause changes to the local ecosystem.

Energy is wasted at every stage of conversion, from when the coal is burned to when the electricity is used in the device required. Energy production is very inefficient.

Burning fossil fuels can cause havoc!

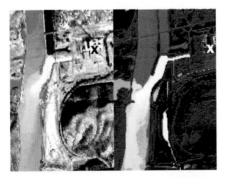

This aerial photo shows the increased temperature of the water outfall from a power station (X) into a river. The version on the right shows hot water as white and yellow, and cooler water as red.

Another example of unwanted heat being released into the atmosphere.

1 Look at the Sankey diagram above. What form of energy is most likely to be wasted at the various stages? ▲

2 The wasted energy at some stages may be made up of different varieties. What are they? ▲

3 In a table, list as many advantages and disadvantages as you can for
a conventional power stations
b hydroelectric power stations.

4 Compare the impact on the environment of conventional and hydroelectric power stations.

5 **Try to find out** what percentage of energy supplied to a power station is wasted in its conversion to electricity.

33

At present, most of world's energy is supplied by fuels like coal, oil, gas, and uranium. But these fuels won't last forever. They are **non-renewable**. Some fuel supplies may even run out during your lifetime.

The bar chart below shows you how long present supplies of fuel are expected to last. Of course, the chart could change. If everyone decided to use fuels more sensibly, they would last longer.

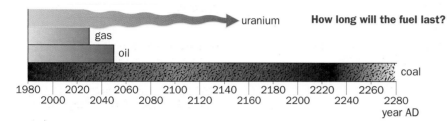

How long will the fuel last?

uranium / gas / oil / coal

1980 2000 2020 2040 2060 2080 2100 2120 2140 2160 2180 2200 2220 2240 2260 2280 year AD

When the fuels begin to run out, there could be problems. That is why scientists and engineers are working hard to find ways of getting useful energy from new energy sources. They are trying to find ways

- to use the moving energy of the wind and waves to turn generators to make electricity
- to use the Sun's heat energy to heat homes, and to make cheap photocells to change its light energy to electricity
- to use the heat energy of hot rocks which lie just below the Earth's surface
- to control the tremendous energy from nuclear fusion reactions, which produce temperatures as high as those in the Sun
- to produce new fuels, such as hydrogen from water or alcohol from sugar cane or other plants.

By the time the fuels run out, at least some of these problems should have been solved!

DiD YOU KNOW?

- A nuclear fusion reaction produces a temperature of 100 000 000 °C.
- Plans have been made to build windmills as tall as skyscrapers, with blades 50 m long.

1 Why could there be a serious energy crisis in the future? ▲
2 When are the following fuels expected to run out:
  a oil?   b gas?
  c uranium? d coal? ▲
3 What does a photocell do? ▲
4 Which energy sources will still be available when you are 70?
5 Why would it be very useful to be able to make
  a hydrogen from water?
  b alcohol from sugar cane?
6 **Try to find out** some ways of saving fuel.

Other methods of energy production

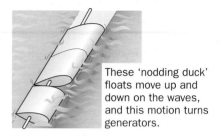

These 'nodding duck' floats move up and down on the waves, and this motion turns generators.

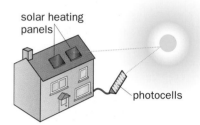

solar heating panels

photocells

A windmill like this was built on Orkney.

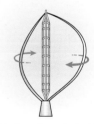

This is a French design for a windmill.

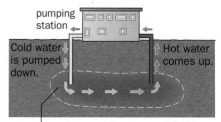

Heat from the hot water is used to heat homes.

pumping station

Cold water is pumped down.

Hot water comes up.

The hot rock is broken up so that water can flow through.

Because fossil fuels will eventually run out, scientists are developing other ways of generating energy. Using nuclear energy in a power station is one way. Other methods include using the Sun's energy directly, or using the energy from the wind and waves or from plants (where the energy originally comes from the Sun!).

These 'alternative' energy sources are all **renewable**. However much energy you use, the source does not run out. Renewable energy sources can reduce the damage to the environment. They don't produce pollution or nasty waste products. But they each have their own disadvantages.

Energy source	For	Against
Hydroelectric energy Potential energy is stored in water in reservoirs high in the hills. When water is released, it flows down pipes, and the potential energy is converted into kinetic energy. This is used to turn turbines and so generate electricity.	Every time it rains, there is more water to provide more energy.	Large dams have to be built and valleys may need to be flooded to provide the store of water. This may destroy wildlife habitats (including rainforests). It can only be used in wet, hilly regions.
Solar energy Solar energy can be used in two ways: ⮑ collector panels are used to convert the Sun's energy directly into heat energy ⮑ panels of solar cells are used to convert the Sun's energy into electrical energy.	Whenever the Sun shines, heat energy is produced. However much energy you use, more energy will be produced. Energy from collector panels is produced quite cheaply. Solar cells are made from silicon, which is an abundant element.	It only works when the Sun shines. Collector panels are only useful for producing small increases in temperature (e.g. warming water). Solar cells are still quite expensive to produce. For larger amounts of energy, large areas of solar cells are needed.
Wind energy The Sun heats up the land and this results in winds forming. The wind drives windmills or wind generators. These produce mechanical or electrical energy.	Whenever the wind blows, energy is produced. However much energy you use, more energy will be produced.	It only works efficiently in windy places. For large amounts of energy, very many generators covering a large area are needed.
Wave energy The wind forms waves on the ocean. The energy in the waves is used to produce electricity using generators.	Whenever there are waves, energy is produced. However much energy you use, more energy will be produced.	Wave generators only work efficiently in exposed sea areas (e.g. around the north-west coast of Scotland). For large amounts of energy, many kilometres of wave generators are needed.

1 What does renewable mean? ▲
2 What is the advantage of using renewable energy sources? ▲
3 *We depend on the Sun for most of our energy needs.* Explain how this is true for
  a the sources above
  b fossil fuels. ▲
4 Why does it make sense to look for alternatives to fossil fuels to provide our energy?
5 **Try to find out** more about generating energy from the wind.

Wind generators

DID YOU KNOW?
⮑ We use more electrical energy during the day than at night.
⮑ At Sloy, on Loch Lomond, water falls from a high-level reservoir to produce electricity. The reservoir is used to regulate the water level in Loch Lomond to prevent flooding.

Energy source	For	Against
Tidal energy The movement of the tides, produced by the gravitational pull of the Moon (and to a smaller extent, the Sun), is used to drive turbines to produce electricity.	Whenever there are tides, energy is produced. However much energy you use, more energy will be produced at the next tide.	It only works efficiently in areas with a large tidal range (e.g. the River Severn estuary). A large area of water must be enclosed by a barrage. The high water levels behind the barrage can alter wildlife habitats.
Geothermal energy In some areas, the high temperatures within the Earth heat up rocks close to the surface. Cold water is pumped into these rocks and the hot water produced can be used for local heating schemes.	Whenever there are hot rocks near the Earth's surface, energy can be produced. However much energy you use, more is available.	It's only possible in areas where there are hot rocks near the Earth's surface (e.g. certain parts of Iceland and New Zealand).

Energy from biomass

Energy can also be obtained from biomass. A variety of processes can be used. Each involves using the energy stored in living plant materials. Remember that plants use the Sun's energy to convert carbon dioxide and water into sugars (photosynthesis).

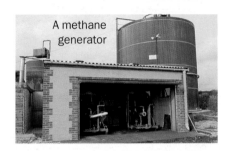

A methane generator

Growing plants to burn Plants, especially fast-growing trees, can be grown for fuel.	These sources are renewable. However much you use, you can grow some more.	The burning fuel does release carbon dioxide into the atmosphere. This tends to be only small quantities.
Growing plants for oil The seeds of certain plants such as sunflowers and oil seed rape contain high levels of oil. This oil can be used as fuel as well as in foods.	In Brazil, alcohol from sugar was mixed with petrol and used as a fuel for specially converted car engines.	For large energy production, large land areas would be needed. Artificial fertilizers might have to be used.
Fermenting biomass Sewage products, dung, and plants can be fermented to produce methane gas. The sugar from sugar cane can be fermented to produce alcohol.		For certain schemes, a suitable climate is important. Remember that burning large quantities of existing forest timber can have long-term effects on the atmosphere.

1 Do tidal energy and geothermal energy depend on the Sun? ▲
2 What damage can tidal energy schemes do to the environment? ▲
3 What advantage does using biomass have over fossil fuels? ▲
4 What are likely to be the main impacts on the environment from using energy from biomass?
5 One method of making more efficient use of our energy sources would be to use less energy! **Try to find out** how a 'save it' scheme could reduce the energy used in
  a house heating and lighting
  b transport.

DID YOU KNOW?
- One 'petroleum nut' tree can produce 50 litres of oil each year for cooking or lighting.
- 1200 ha of the fast-growing 'ipilipil' tree can produce in a year the same energy as one million barrels of crude oil.

NIMBY – Not In My BackYard

Respond to the various statements made in the school playground.

As you go round this energy trail, you will learn something about Britain's
energy supplies in the next 50 years or so. You can use dice and make the
trail into a game if you like. If not, jump around the trail two squares at a
time. When you land on a red or green square, do what you're told!

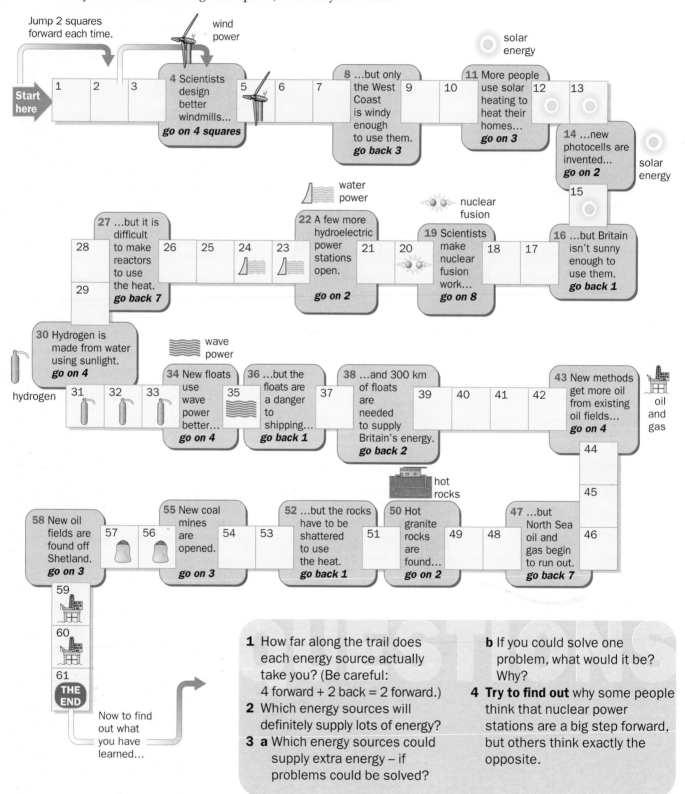

Jump 2 squares forward each time.

wind power

solar energy

Start here

1 2 3

4 Scientists design better windmills...
go on 4 squares

5 6 7

8 ...but only the West Coast is windy enough to use them.
go back 3

9 10

11 More people use solar heating to heat their homes...
go on 3

12 13

solar energy

14 ...new photocells are invented...
go on 2

15

solar energy

water power

nuclear fusion

27 ...but it is difficult to make reactors to use the heat.
go back 7

28 29

26 25 24 23

22 A few more hydroelectric power stations open.
go on 2

21 20

19 Scientists make nuclear fusion work...
go on 8

18 17

16 ...but Britain isn't sunny enough to use them.
go back 1

30 Hydrogen is made from water using sunlight.
go on 4

hydrogen

31 32 33

wave power

34 New floats use wave power better...
go on 4

35

36 ...but the floats are a danger to shipping...
go back 1

37

38 ...and 300 km of floats are needed to supply Britain's energy.
go back 2

39 40 41 42

43 New methods get more oil from existing oil fields...
go on 4

oil and gas

44

hot rocks

45

58 New oil fields are found off Shetland.
go on 3

57 56

55 New coal mines are opened.
go on 3

54 53

52 ...but the rocks have to be shattered to use the heat.
go back 1

51

50 Hot granite rocks are found...
go on 2

49 48

47 ...but North Sea oil and gas begin to run out.
go back 7

46

59

60

61

THE END

Now to find out what you have learned...

QUESTIONS

1 How far along the trail does each energy source actually take you? (Be careful: 4 forward + 2 back = 2 forward.)
2 Which energy sources will definitely supply lots of energy?
3 a Which energy sources could supply extra energy – if problems could be solved?

b If you could solve one problem, what would it be? Why?
4 Try to find out why some people think that nuclear power stations are a big step forward, but others think exactly the opposite.

The magnificent Golden Eagle was once found throughout the British Isles, but now only a few pairs breed outside Scotland. With a wingspan of 2 m or more, it is one of the largest birds of prey in Britain. The most likely places to find Golden Eagles here are the isles of Islay, Mull, and Skye and some of the more remote Scottish glens. Almost 15% (approximately 500 pairs) of the Golden Eagles' current European population is in Scotland. To find out facts such as these, we need to understand how to categorize and identify animals, and in this chapter, you will see how scientists set about studying living things, whether animals or plants.

Organism is the scientific name for a living thing. You are an organism living on the planet Earth.

Millions and millions of other organisms live on Earth with you. Very many of these belong to the group of **animals**. Many more belong to the group of **plants**.

Here are some of the things which animals are able to do:

Animals **move**.

Animals **feed**.

Animals **grow**.

Animals breathe to get oxygen for **respiration**.

Animals **react** to things about them.

Animals **reproduce** (they produce others like themselves).

Many people think that plants are completely different from animals, but they are wrong. Plants also need **food** to live, but they make it for themselves. They excrete waste materials and gases. Plants **grow** and **reproduce** too. They **respire** and **react** to things around them. Even though a whole plant cannot **move** from place to place on its own, some parts of plants can. For example some plants can open their flowers when the sun shines.

Animals **excrete** waste.

1 Animals and plants are organisms. What does this mean? ▲
2 In what ways are animals and plants like each other? ▲
3 Make a set of animals and a set of plants from this list: *cat, carrot, corn, eagle, whale, toadstool, seaweed, jellyfish.*
4 How would you react if you sat on a drawing pin?
5 **Try to find out**
  a why plants grow upwards
  b if there are signs of life on other planets.

DID YOU KNOW?
- ➲ Over 1 500 000 different kinds of animals have been found on Earth. Most of these are insects.
- ➲ So far, about 300 000 different kinds of plants have been found on Earth

The things that all animals and plants can do are called **life processes**. Living things have seven life processes – these are shown on the previous page.

Most of the life processes take place in particular parts of an animal or a plant called **organs**.

Organs of the human body

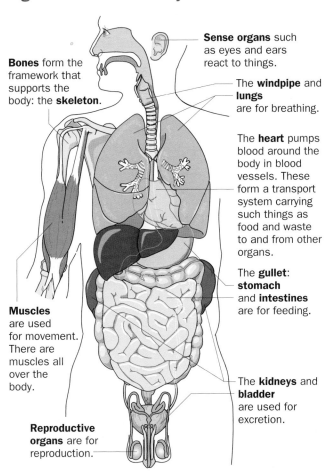

Bones form the framework that supports the body: the **skeleton**.

Sense organs such as eyes and ears react to things.

The **windpipe** and **lungs** are for breathing.

The **heart** pumps blood around the body in blood vessels. These form a transport system carrying such things as food and waste to and from other organs.

The **gullet**: **stomach** and **intestines** are for feeding.

Muscles are used for movement. There are muscles all over the body.

The **kidneys** and **bladder** are used for excretion.

Reproductive organs are for reproduction.

Growth happens all over the body until a person becomes an adult.

Plant organs

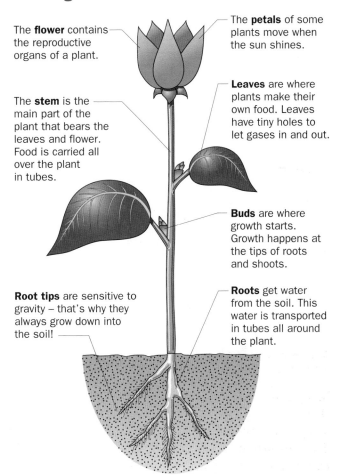

The **flower** contains the reproductive organs of a plant.

The **petals** of some plants move when the sun shines.

The **stem** is the main part of the plant that bears the leaves and flower. Food is carried all over the plant in tubes.

Leaves are where plants make their own food. Leaves have tiny holes to let gases in and out.

Buds are where growth starts. Growth happens at the tips of roots and shoots.

Root tips are sensitive to gravity – that's why they always grow down into the soil!

Roots get water from the soil. This water is transported in tubes all around the plant.

Big plants, like trees, get rid of waste by putting it in leaves and dropping them at certain times of the year.

1 a What are life processes?
 b Where do they take place? ▲
2 Which life processes take place all over the human body? ▲
3 Name the organs which are involved in feeding in humans. ▲
4 a Describe how water gets from the roots to other parts of a plant.
 b What organs do the same kind of job in humans?
5 Oak trees lose their leaves in the autumn. Pine trees lose their leaves all year round. Explain why this happens.
6 Try to find out the name of a plant that has sensitive leaves.

DID YOU KNOW?

⮑ If you put a piece of celery in coloured water, you will see the water rising slowly up the stem. To see the tubes that carry the water, cut a thin slice off the end and look at it with a hand lens. The tubes will be coloured; the surrounding cells won't be.

You don't have to be a brilliant scientist to see that people are different. Look at the pupils in your science class. Some are tall, some are short. Some are thin, some are fat. Some have freckles, some don't. Some have brown hair, some blond, some auburn, some black, and some ginger. There are different eye and skin colours too. The world is so much more interesting because of the variety or **variation** of different people in it.

The chart shows the variety of pupils in Science class AZ.

Joe can roll his tongue…

…but Angela can't! Can you?

Pupil's name	Height (cm)	Shoe size	Hair colour	Eye colour	Left-or right-handed	Freckles or no freckles
Mark	153	4	blond	grey	right	no freckles
Liz	161	5	auburn	blue	right	freckles
Joe	150	2	brown	blue	right	no freckles
Joan	151	2	brown	green	left	freckles
David	151	5	blond	blue	right	freckles
Angela	150	4	black	brown	right	no freckles
Len	153	4	black	grey	left	freckles
Katherine	162	6	brown	brown	right	no freckles
Ian	161	4	brown	blue	left	freckles
Heather	162	5	blond	blue	right	freckles
Jim	161	7	blond	green	right	no freckles
Fatima	161	5	black	brown	right	no freckles
Alan	154	5	brown	brown	right	freckles
Carol	159	5	brown	blue	right	freckles
Austin	155	5	ginger	blue	left	no freckles
Gwen	151	3	brown	brown	right	freckles
Janet	154	4	auburn	green	left	freckles
Ashad	158	6	black	brown	right	no freckles

1 Write down
   a Len's height
   b Joan's eye colour
   c Ian's hair colour. ▲
2 What is the most common
   a shoe size?
   b eye colour?
3 Describe
   a Alan
   b Angela. ▲

4 Which pupil is most like you, and why?
5 How would this table of information have changed three years later when the class was 4 AZ?
6 **Try to find out** if the tallest-ever man would have banged his head on your classroom doorframe.

DID YOU KNOW?
- The tallest-ever human (a man) measured 272 cm.
- The shortest-ever human (a woman) measured 61 cm.

People can be very different.

If you measure the height of lots of pupils of your age you can use the data to plot a frequency graph like this. The more pupils you measure, the better the graph will be. Notice how the graph is in the shape of a bell. This bell shape is called a **normal distribution curve**.

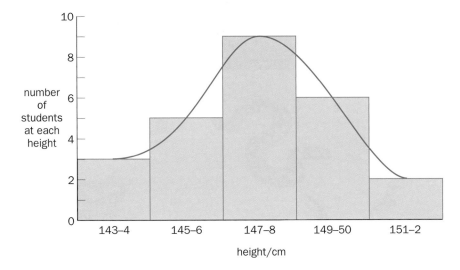

There is variation in plant roots.

The average height of the pupils is in the middle of the curve. Most pupils will have height close to this average. Only a few pupils are really tall or really short.

Features such as height and weight are examples of **continuous variation**. You could fit anywhere within a continuous range of possible measurements.

Some features, however, are distinct: there is no continuous range. Your sex is a good example. You are either male or female – there is no other option. Eye colour, tongue rolling, and ear lobes are other examples of what we call **discontinuous variation**. You either have the feature or you haven't – you either can or you can't!

These leaves show variation as well.

Our surroundings or activities can also affect variation. Height and weight can be affected by what sort of food we eat or how much we eat. Exposure to sunlight affects the colour of our skin – no matter what colour it is to begin with. This sort of variation is called **acquired variation** because people acquire these characteristics as a result of what they do during their lives.

1 There is variation in your class. What does this mean? ▲
2 Give some examples of variation in humans. ▲
3 Which of the following are examples of
  a continuous
  b discontinuous variation?
  weight, tongue rolling, height, eye colour, ear lobes ▲
4 Sally has a scar on her knee. She got it playing hockey. The other students in her class don't have scars. What sort of variation is this?
5 **Try to find out** how many different eye colours there are.

DID YOU KNOW?

➲ Human birth weight can be influenced by the mother's diet and whether or not she smoked during pregnancy.

➲ In plants, the amount of light, water, and suitable temperature can affect the size of fruit.

Great Craggie is an island with lots of animals on it. The sea round about it has more animals still.

You can see a few of these animals in the pictures below:

It is often useful to put animals of the same type into groups called **sets**. Here are three different ways of doing this:

D E H O N

A set of animals found in the stream

1 You can make sets by thinking of where the animals live:
  a Put all the animals which live on the land in one set.
  b Put all the animals which live in the water into another set.
  c Which animals don't fit properly into either of these sets? Why?

2 You can make sets by thinking of what the animals can do:
  a Make a set of animals which can fly.
  b Pick an 'odd one out' from this set. Why did you choose it?

3 You can make sets by thinking of what the animals are like:
  Make sets of animals with
  a feathers
  b fur or hair
  c fins
  d backbones.

4 Which way makes the best sets of animals? Why?

DiD YOU KNOW?

➲ Only three kinds of snakes live in Britain: the grass snake, the smooth snake, and the viper, or adder.

➲ The adder is the only poisonous British snake.

➲ All of these animals and humans are vertebrates: they all have backbones.

Biologists are scientists who study living things. They have worked out a good way of putting animals and plants into sets. They call it **classification**. The biggest sets are called **kingdoms**. The two biggest kingdoms are the Plant Kingdom and the Animal Kingdom.

DID YOU KNOW?

There are three other kingdoms. These are the

- ➲ Kingdom Prokaryotae (single-celled organisms that don't have a nucleus)
- ➲ Kingdom Protoctista (single-celled organisms that have a nucleus)
- ➲ Kingdom Fungi (they feed on dead things and make them decompose).

Plant Kingdom

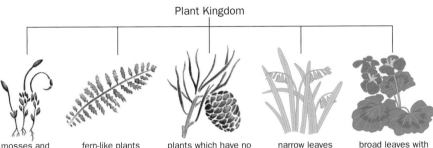

| mosses and liverworts (*Bryophyta*) e.g. moss | fern-like plants (*Pteridophyta*) e.g. fern | plants which have no ovary and produce naked seeds (*Coniferophyta*) e.g. pine | narrow leaves with narrow veins (*Monocotyledons*) e.g. bluebell | broad leaves with a network of veins (*Dicotyledons*) e.g. geranium |

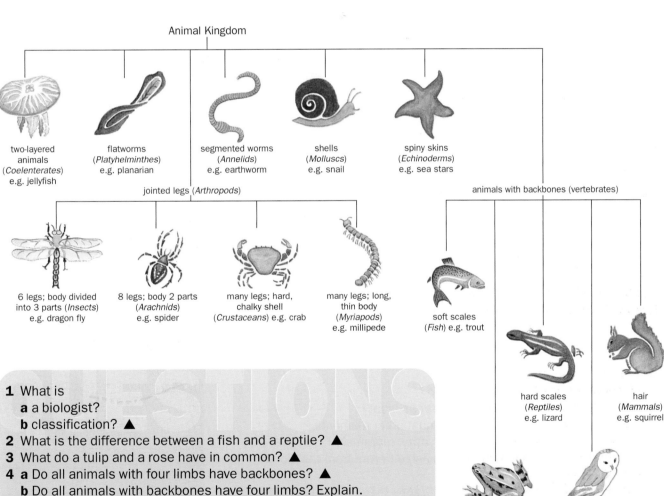

Animal Kingdom

two-layered animals (*Coelenterates*) e.g. jellyfish

flatworms (*Platyhelminthes*) e.g. planarian

segmented worms (*Annelids*) e.g. earthworm

shells (*Molluscs*) e.g. snail

spiny skins (*Echinoderms*) e.g. sea stars

jointed legs (*Arthropods*)

animals with backbones (vertebrates)

6 legs; body divided into 3 parts (*Insects*) e.g. dragon fly

8 legs; body 2 parts (*Arachnids*) e.g. spider

many legs; hard, chalky shell (*Crustaceans*) e.g. crab

many legs; long, thin body (*Myriapods*) e.g. millipede

soft scales (*Fish*) e.g. trout

hard scales (*Reptiles*) e.g. lizard

hair (*Mammals*) e.g. squirrel

smooth, moist skin (*Amphibians*) e.g. frog

feathers (*Birds*) e.g. owl

1 What is
  a a biologist?
  b classification? ▲
2 What is the difference between a fish and a reptile? ▲
3 What do a tulip and a rose have in common? ▲
4 a Do all animals with four limbs have backbones? ▲
  b Do all animals with backbones have four limbs? Explain.
5 Which set does each of these living things fit into:
  lobster, butterfly, dog, human, fir tree, daffodil, primrose?
6 Try to find out the names of some more
  a molluscs
  b algae.

It pays to look closely at an animal before you put it into a set. Appearances can be deceiving!

Here are two animals which you might find in the sea round Great Craggie. They both look like fish, but one of them does not belong to the set of fish.

Animal **G** is covered with very small scales, and it has fins. Its blood temperature changes with the temperature of the water round it. It stays under water without coming up for air. The young are not fed by their mother. Animal **G** is a **fish**. It is a **basking shark**.

But animal **F** has no scales or fins on its body (although, to be fair, you won't see hair or fur either). Its blood stays at a steady temperature. After 15 minutes under water, it has to come up for air. The young feed on their mothers' milk. And so animal **F**, a **dolphin**, is a **mammal**, not a fish.

Animal **K** is another which could confuse you, particularly as it only comes out at night. As it flies around, it looks like a small bird. But it has fur, not feathers. Its blood temperature is constant. The females have milk glands. Animal **K** is a **bat**, the only mammal which can really fly.

F

G

K

1 Why is a shark put in the set of fish?
2 **a** Why is a dolphin put in the same set as a bat?
   b How is the dolphin different from most other mammals?
   c How is the bat different from most other mammals?
3 **a** How is the blood temperature of a fish different from the blood temperature of a mammal?
   b Why must Arctic fish produce 'anti-freeze chemicals' to survive in icy waters?
   c Why can whales (mammals) survive without these chemicals?
4 A fish can use the oxygen which is dissolved in the water, but a dolphin can't. What difference does that make?
5 **Try to find out** some things which dolphins have been trained to do.

DID YOU KNOW?

➜ Next to man and other primates, the dolphin is considered to be the most intelligent creature.

➜ Arctic fish produce 'anti-freeze chemicals' to help them survive in ice-cold waters.

What do we do when we want to know the name of an animal or plant we don't recognize? The answer is to use a **key**. A key is a series of questions we ask ourselves. Each answer leads to another question. This goes on until eventually the name of the organism is found.

Here is a simple key which will help you to name the four 'unknown' animals shown opposite.

1 **a** If the mammal has flippers, it is a **dolphin**.
   b But if the mammal has legs, *you must go to 2*.
2 **a** If the mammal has wings, it is a **bat**.
   b But if the mammal has no wings, *you must go to 3*.
3 **a** If the mammal has a bushy tail, it is a **squirrel**.
   b But if the mammal has a long narrow tail, it is an otter.

The correct answers are: A = otter   F = dolphin   I = squirrel   K = bat

Now name these reptiles, fish, and amphibians using the key below:

mammals

reptiles

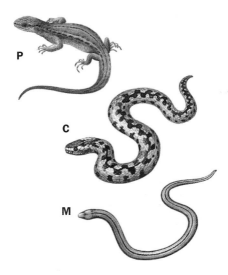

fish

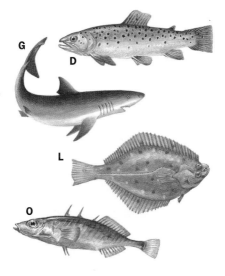

amphibians

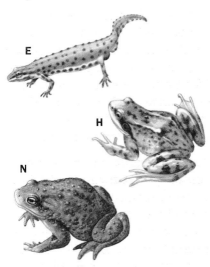

Reptile with:
1 **a** legs   → **lizard**.
   b no legs   → *go to 2*
2 **a** zigzag pattern   → **adder**.
       on skin
   b no zigzag   → **slow**
       pattern on skin   **worm**.
Name animals **P, C,** *and* **M**.

Fish with:
1 **a** five gill slits   → **basking**
       showing   **shark.**
   b gills covered   → *go to 2*
2 **a** 3 sharp spines   → **stickleback**.
   b no spines   → *go to 3*
3 **a** round body   → **trout**.
   b flat body   → **flounder**.
Name animals **G, L, D,** *and* **O**.

Amphibians with:
1 **a** tail   → **newt**.
   b no tail   → *go to 2*
2 **a** smooth skin   → **frog**.
   b warty skin   → **toad**.
Name animals **E, H,** *and* **N**.

⮑ The picture shows four leaves. Make up a key to help someone name these leaves.

beech   oak   horse chestnut   mountain ash

In the drawings, you can see the flowers from six plants which grow on Great Craggie.

Here is a different kind of key. It will help you identify the plants by their flowers. The key works in just the same way as the one on the previous page, but it is written in the form of a flow chart. It will help you to name the plants from Great Craggie.

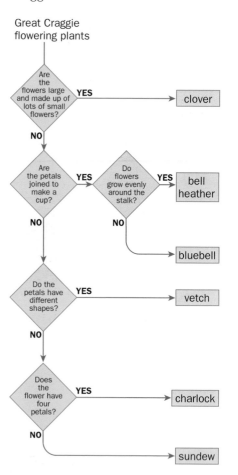

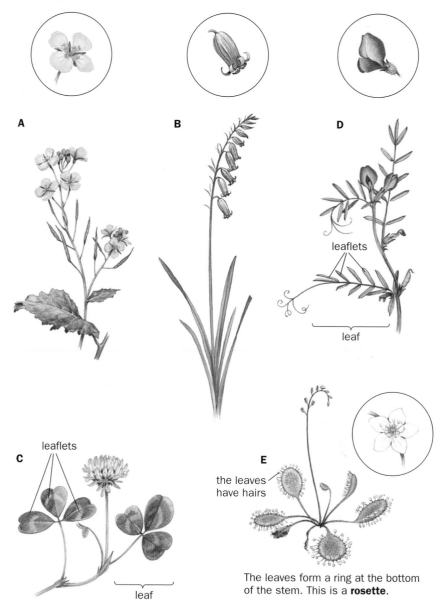

A

B

D

leaflets

leaf

C

leaflets

leaf

E

the leaves have hairs

The leaves form a ring at the bottom of the stem. This is a **rosette**.

F

whorls

Great Craggie flowering plants

Are the flowers large and made up of lots of small flowers? — **YES** → clover

NO

Are the petals joined to make a cup? — **YES** → Do flowers grow evenly around the stalk? — **YES** → bell heather

NO — → bluebell

NO

Do the petals have different shapes? — **YES** → vetch

NO

Does the flower have four petals? — **YES** → charlock

NO — → sundew

1 Why are keys useful? ▲
2 Explain how to use a key. ▲
3 Suggest why you can't always identify plants by their flowers.
4 Use the flower key to answer these questions:
   a What does a charlock flower look like?
   b In what way is a clover flower different from all the other flowers?
   c What are the names of plants **A** to **F**?
5 Make a key to identify the plants by their leaves.

Counting plants

Think how difficult it would be to count every plant in just a small part of a field. To make things easier we can use a method called **sampling**. A sample is a small part of an area that is studied very closely. When you choose a sample, you must try to make sure that it is typical of the whole area. For example, it's no good studying just a worn out goal mouth when you want to survey a whole football pitch!

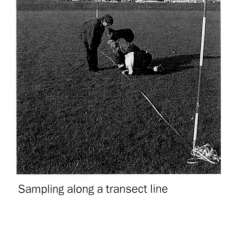
Sampling along a transect line

Sampling along a transect line
A transect line is a piece of string or measuring tape stretched tightly between two poles across the survey area. At regular intervals, e.g. 1 m, you identify and record the names of the plants close to the line. Your results can be presented in the form of a bar chart like this:

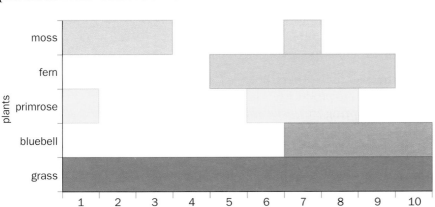

Sampling with a quadrat
A quadrat is a sort of grid. Every square in the grid has the same area. The quadrat shown in the picture is 0.5 m square, but they can be bigger. You put the quadrat on the ground at random – you could drop it carefully over your shoulder as you walk across the survey area! The plants inside the quadrat are identified, and then you count up how many squares contain each plant species. For example, in the diagram, daisies are found in $\frac{13}{25}$ squares of the quadrat. Multiply this by 4 and you get $\frac{52}{100}$ or 52%. In this example, daisies occur 52% of the time. Not only do you know when a plant is present but also how often it occurs in your sample.

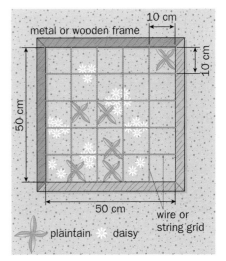
A quadrat

1 a What is a sample?
  b Why must you be careful when choosing a sample? ▲
2 a What is a transect line?
  b Explain how you would use a transect line to sample an area of school field. ▲
3 In the graph above, which point on the transect line has
  a most plants?
  b fewest plants?

4 a Describe a quadrat.
  b Work out how often plantain occurs in the quadrat shown in the diagram.
5 Give one advantage of sampling with a quadrat rather than a transect line.
6 Try to find out the names of four plants growing on your school field.

DiD YOU KNOW?
⊃ The points on a transect line are called stations.
⊃ Stations can be as close or as far apart as you want – it depends how big the area you are surveying is.

In this chapter you have been able to look at a small part of the wildlife of Great Craggie. There are many other animals and plants on the island.

The pictures show four of the island's resident birds. Resident birds live on the island all the year round. You will see they are different kinds of gulls.

All gulls have webbed feet and strong, hooked beaks. However, two of the islands gulls have black heads, two haven't. The colours of their beaks and legs are different. The birds are closely related to each other, but they are not the same.

Grouping together

Scientists put animals and plants into sets or classification groups. Those organisms which have some common features are put into a set called a **genus**. The gulls in the picture belong to one genus, swans belong to another, falcons to another, and so on. But birds of the same kind are put into a smaller set called a **species**. The pictures show four different species of gull.

Feathers may vary in colour. Some gulls may be heavier than others. But members of the same species can breed with each other to produce fertile young. If members of different species breed, their offspring are sterile and cannot produce young of their own.

Scientific names

Every living thing has a scientific name. Each organism needs a name which is understood all over the world. In Sweden the black-headed gull is called skrattmås; in France it is called mouette rieuse. By using the scientific name, *Larus ridibundus*, all scientists know which bird they are talking about.

The first part of the scientific name is the genus. The second part is the species. The table shows the common names and the scientific names of the four gulls shown in the picture.

A

B

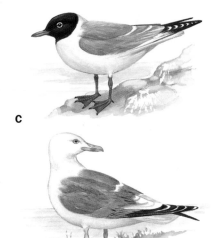

C

D

These are pictures of the four gulls mentioned in the table. Which gull is which?

Common name	Scientific name
herring gull	*Larus argentatus*
lesser black-backed gull	*Larus fuscus*
little gull	*Larus minutus*
black-headed gull	*Larus ridibundus*

1 What is meant by
  a a resident? **b** a genus?
  c a species? ▲
2 Explain why living things are given scientific names. ▲
3 Use a bird book to match the names in the table with the four gulls shown.
4 Budgerigars and canaries are birds which can breed together and produce young. Explain why these offspring are not able to produce young of their own.
5 Try to find out
  a the scientific name of the tawny owl, the starling, and the swallow
  b something about migrating birds.

DID YOU KNOW?

➲ There may be lots of common names for the same animal or plant. The creeping buttercup has 36 different names in Britain alone.

Atoms and molecules

Robert Brown was a Scottish botanist. In 1827, he made a seemingly insignificant observation, that dead pollen grains in a liquid move minutely all the time, a little way here, a little way there, but always unpredictably. This effect, which he found was the same for all tiny particles, not just pollen, came to be known as Brownian motion. Brown and others after him spent many years trying to explain it, but they were unsuccessful. It wasn't until 1905, however, that Albert Einstein was able to give a complete theory about Brownian motion. This theory only worked if it was true that gases and liquids are made up of fast-moving atoms and molecules, whose collisions with pollen grains in a liquid, for example, made them move the way that Brown had observed. This chapter looks further at ideas about atoms and molecules and other evidence that they exist.

Coal, heating oil, and butane are three common fuels. They will help you to understand the differences between solids, liquids, and gases.

The solid state

Coal is a **solid** fuel.

- ➲ A solid cannot move. It stays where it is, unless something, or someone, moves it.
- ➲ A solid keeps its shape – unless it is broken.
- ➲ The volume of a solid always stays the same.

The liquid state

Heating oil is a **liquid** fuel.

- ➲ A liquid can flow.
- ➲ A liquid takes up the shape of its container.
- ➲ The volume of a liquid stays the same.

The gas state

Butane is a **gas** fuel. It is the main fuel used for camping stoves and cigarette lighters.

- ➲ A gas can flow: it will spread out as far as it can.
- ➲ A gas can change shape.
- ➲ The volume of a gas can change, too.

It's difficult to show all of this. Most gases are invisible.

It's a solid, a liquid, or a gas!

All of the substances around you can be put into the set of solids, or the set of liquids, or the set of gases. Solids, liquids, and gases are the **three states of matter**.

1 What are the three states of matter? ▲
2 What can you say about
   a the shape of a solid? **b** the volume of a liquid?
   c the shape of a gas?   **d** the volume of a solid? ▲
3 Make a list of *six* solids, *six* liquids, and *six* gases.
4 If North Sea gas is invisible, how can you tell when gas is leaking?
5 **Try to find out** the names of some other fuels and whether they are solids, liquids, or gases.

DID YOU KNOW?

- ➲ The world depends on huge amounts of fuel and on huge vehicles to carry it. Coal trains in the USA are often over 5 km long. The world's biggest oil tanker is over 400 m long and carries $\frac{1}{2}$ million tonnes of oil.

Solids, liquids, and gases behave very differently. That makes them useful for different jobs. In a car, for example, they all have special jobs to do:

Solids (like steel, plastic, and glass) are used to make the car body. The body has to stay solid to keep its shape.

Liquids (like petrol and diesel) are used as fuels. Liquid fuels flow easily from the tank to the engine.

Gas (air) is used to fill the tyres. A tyre with gas in it can change shape when it hits a bump.

steel

glass

petrol (inside tank)

plastic

air

Changing state

It can be useful, too, to change a substance from one state to another – for example, from solid to liquid, or from liquid to gas:

A car engine is made of iron or aluminium. But it cannot be shaped from a solid lump. Instead, the metal is melted and the red-hot liquid is poured into a mould. The liquid flows into shape. Then it cools and hardens.

The glass for the windows is made in the same kind of way. Red-hot liquid glass is allowed to flow until it forms a sheet. Then it cools and hardens.

Some vehicles use natural gas or petroleum gas as a fuel. It would take up far too much space to store the fuel as a gas. And so it is stored in strong tanks as a liquid. This is changed to a gas when needed.

1 Explain why
  a a car body is mostly made of solids
  b liquids are usually used as car fuel
  c gas is used to fill car tyres. ▲
2 Why do cars not use
  a solid fuel?
  b solid tyres?
3 Why is it useful
  a to make a car engine out of red-hot liquid iron?
  b to store petroleum gas as a liquid? ▲

4 Give some examples of
  a solid objects which are shaped by pouring liquid into a mould
  b gases which are stored as liquids in cylinders.
5 **Try to find out**
  a how plastic objects – like the case of a mobile phone – are made
  b where to get LPG (liquefied petroleum gas) or LNG (liquefied natural gas).

DiD YOU KNOW?
➲ Most of the metal and plastic in a car can be **recycled** (used again) when the car is scrapped. They can be melted and moulded into other things. Old plastic batteries and bumpers, for example, are used to make new ones.

Usually, it's quite easy to decide whether a substance is a solid, a liquid, or a gas. But there are some difficult cases – substances which do not fit easily into one set or another. Take toothpaste, for example. It flows and changes shape when you squeeze the tube. Is it a liquid? When you tip sand out of a barrow, it flows. Does that make it a liquid? What about plasticine? It looks solid, but you can change its shape over and over again. Steam spreads out everywhere, like a gas, but you can see it. Where do these substances fit in?

To deal with these difficult cases, you have to ask the same questions that you asked before – **'does the substance change shape, change volume, or flow?'** (The key opposite should help.) But you then have to do some careful observation. What you have to find out is **what happens when the substance is left on its own.**

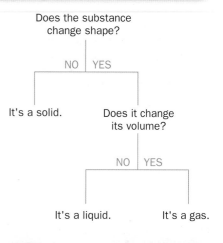

Does the substance change shape?

NO | YES

It's a solid. | Does it change its volume?

NO | YES

It's a liquid. | It's a gas.

Toothpaste does change shape and flow when you squeeze the tube. But once it is on the brush, it doesn't flow, and it keeps its shape. That's because it is a **solid.**

Sand is a **solid** also – even though dry sand flows easily. When you look at grains of sand through a microscope, you will see that each one has a definite shape – and keeps it.

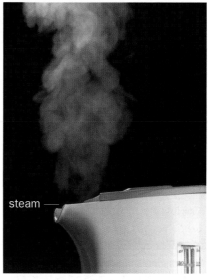

steam —

You can see white clouds spreading out from a boiling kettle because they are made of tiny droplets of water. The real steam is the invisible **gas** at the kettle spout.

1 If you are trying to find out if a substance is a solid, a liquid, or a gas,
  a what question should you ask yourself? ▲
  b what observation should you make? ▲
2 Sand flows. Why is it called a solid? ▲
3 Are these solids, liquids, or gases? Explain your answer.
  jelly, perfume, tomato sauce, paper, the vapour from perfume, sugar.
4 What is
  a a fluid?
  b a powder? ▲
5 Find
  a the fluids
  b the powders mentioned on this page.
6 **Try to find out** what fluidized coal is, and where it is used.

DID YOU KNOW?

➲ Any substance (gas or liquid) which can flow on its own is called a **fluid**. A crushed-up solid is a **powder**.

➲ Plasticine is used to make models for some cartoons. It can take a year's work to make a half-hour cartoon.

It's difficult to believe, but it's true: all solids, liquids, and gases are made up of tiny particles. The smallest particles are called **atoms**. A **molecule** is a group of atoms joined together.

Scientists have built up models of the atoms and molecules in solids, liquids, and gases. You can see them pictured below.

atoms join

to give a molecule

Molecular models

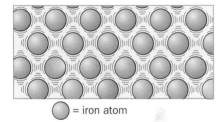

= iron atom

This is a model of the atoms in a lump of **solid** iron.

Notice that the atoms are:
1 arranged in rows
2 close together
3 held together tightly
4 not able to change places
5 vibrating (moving backwards and forwards).

Scientists think that these are good models for all solids, liquid, and gases. You can use the models to explain lots of things, such as
⊃ *why liquids flow but solids don't*
⊃ *why gases squash more easily than solids.*

You can see the explanations alongside.

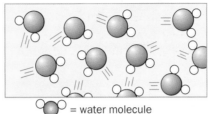

= water molecule

This is a model of the molecules in a drop of **liquid** water.

Notice that the molecules are:
1 not arranged in any particular way
2 close together
3 not so tightly held together as in solids
4 moving about and changing places.

Why solids *can't* flow

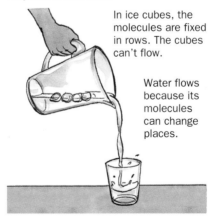

In ice cubes, the molecules are fixed in rows. The cubes can't flow.

Water flows because its molecules can change places.

= oxygen molecule

This is a model of the molecules in oxygen **gas**.

Notice that the molecules are:
1 not arranged in any particular way
2 far apart
3 very weakly held together
4 moving very fast in all directions.

Why gases *can* be squashed easily

Air can be easily squashed. Air molecules have lots of space between them.

Iron can't be easily squashed. Its atoms are close together.

1 What is meant by
  a an atom? **b** a molecule? ▲
2 Which of the following phrases describe atoms and molecules in **a** a solid **b** a liquid
  c a gas? ▲
  close together
  changing places
  tightly held together
  far apart

3 Why do
  a ice cubes not flow?
  b beach balls squash easily? ▲
4 Why do
  a gases spread quickly?
  b solids keep their shapes?
5 **Try to find out** the name of the hardest solid.

...about the tiny atoms and molecules?

Party balloons always go down – even when they are tightly tied. The air inside always escapes.

Scientists know that the balloon skin has tiny holes in it. The air escapes through the holes. It can do this because it is made up of tiny particles that are small enough to get through the holes.

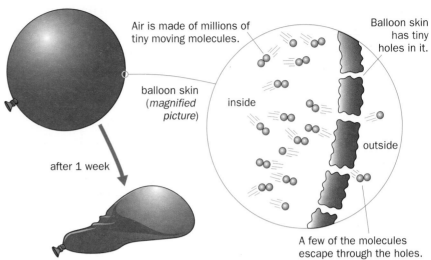

Air is made of millions of tiny moving molecules.

balloon skin (*magnified picture*)

after 1 week

Balloon skin has tiny holes in it.

inside

outside

A few of the molecules escape through the holes.

...about the moving atoms and molecules in gases?

Gases mix through each other. You can see this happen if one of the gases is coloured. You can smell this happening when the top is taken off a perfume bottle or a stink bomb is dropped.

The gases spread out and mix through each other because their atoms and molecules are moving about. When one substance spreads through another like this, we call it **diffusion**.

Diffusion: Stink bomb gas quickly spreads through the air.

Diffusion:

❶ The top cylinder contains air, the bottom one bromine. They are separated with a glass plate.

❷ When the plate is removed, diffusion makes the air molecules move into the bromine jar and the bromine molecules move into the air jar.

❸ A mixture of bromine and air.

1 Why does a balloon go down quickly when you stick a pin in it? ▲
2 Why does a balloon go down even when it is tightly tied? ▲
3 Give *one* piece of evidence which suggests that atoms and molecules are tiny. ▲
4 Give *two* pieces of evidence which suggest that atoms and molecules move about in a gas.
5 What is meant by diffusion? ▲
6 **Try to find out** how long it takes for perfume molecules to travel 3 metres. (Do an experiment.)

DiD YOU KNOW?
➲ Gas molecules can move very fast – up to 2000 metres per second. But they can only travel tiny distances before they bump into other molecules.

...about moving molecules in liquids?

Diffusion can also take place in liquids. When a dye crystal is added to water, it dissolves. Then the coloured dye molecules mix with the moving water molecules.

Diffusion can also take place in a gel (like jelly). A gel is made of tiny particles of solid spread through a liquid. It doesn't flow, but dye molecules can move through it.

The dye diffuses through the water. It's quicker when the water is hot.

The dye diffuses through the gel very slowly.

...about the spaces between atoms and molecules?

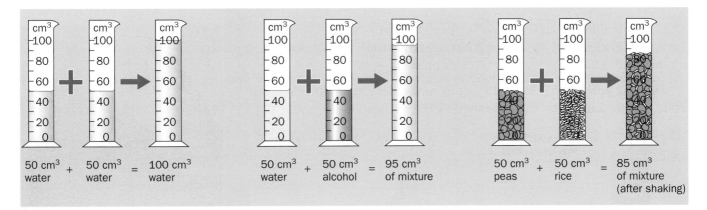

| 50 cm³ water + 50 cm³ water = 100 cm³ water | 50 cm³ water + 50 cm³ alcohol = 95 cm³ of mixture | 50 cm³ peas + 50 cm³ rice = 85 cm³ of mixture (after shaking) |

When you mix alcohol and water, the volume seems to shrink. You can explain this 'disappearing volume' by saying that

the molecules in a liquid have spaces between them.

When the alcohol and water are mixed, water molecules fit into some of the spaces between the alcohol molecules. This makes the volume less than you would expect. If you look at what happens when you mix peas and rice, you can see that this makes sense.

◯ = pea

⬭ = rice

The rice fits into the spaces between the peas. This makes the volume less.

QUESTIONS

1 Give *two* pieces of evidence that the molecules in a liquid are moving.
2 Give *one* piece of evidence that the molecules in a gel move slowly. ▲
3 Why is the final volume not 100 cm³
   a when 50 cm³ peas and 50 cm³ rice are mixed together? ▲
   b when 50 cm³ water and 50 cm³ alcohol are mixed together? ▲
4 **a** Why should you stir tea when you put sugar in it?
   b What would happen if you didn't stir it?
5 **Try to find out** what a hair drier diffuser does.

DID YOU KNOW?

➲ It can take a very long time for diffusion to take place in a liquid. A lump of sugar dissolves quite quickly in water. But if the water is not stirred, it can take weeks for the sugar molecules to spread completely through the water molecules.

When you blow up a balloon, it's the air pressure inside which makes the balloon skin stretch. You blow millions and millions of air molecules into the balloon. They fly around inside the balloon in all directions. Many of them bounce off the inside of the balloon rubber.

Whenever a molecule bounces off the balloon rubber, it gives the rubber a tiny push. Millions of tiny pushes add up to give the air pressure which stretches the balloon skin. **Air pressure is produced by air molecules bouncing off a surface.**

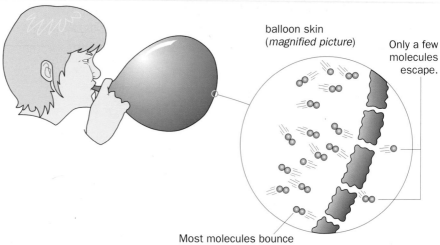

balloon skin (*magnified picture*)

Only a few molecules escape.

Most molecules bounce off the inside of the balloon skin.

There are air molecules bouncing off you and the things around you. Everything is affected by air pressure. The bigger the number of air molecules bouncing off a surface, the bigger is the air pressure on it.

It's amazing how much pressure these tiny molecules can produce. You can make a strong can collapse just by pumping the air out of it.

This can is full of air. The air presses out. The air outside presses in. The can keeps its shape because the air pressure on the inside is equal to the air pressure on the outside.

The same can (really empty!). There is almost no air inside to press out. The air pressure on the outside makes the can collapse.

A barometer is used to measure air pressure. People often use it to try forecast the weather.

1 What produces air pressure? When is the air pressure on a surface large? ▲

2 How can you increase the air pressure inside your bicycle tyres?

3 If you empty out the oil from a can, the can keeps its shape. Why? Why does the can collapse when the air is pumped out of it? ▲

4 Do you think that the pressure is greater inside or outside a blown up balloon? Explain your answer.

5 What is a barometer used for? ▲

6 **Try to find out**
   a why airliners need to have pressurized cabins
   b the types of weather we get when air pressure is high.

Solids, liquids, and gases all **expand** (take up more space) when you heat them. When they are cooled, the opposite happens. They all contract (get smaller).

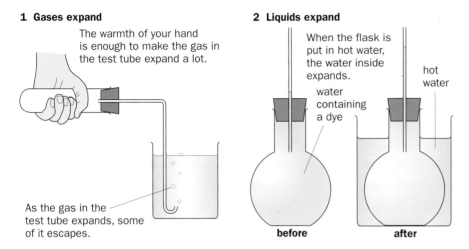

1 Gases expand

The warmth of your hand is enough to make the gas in the test tube expand a lot.

As the gas in the test tube expands, some of it escapes.

2 Liquids expand

When the flask is put in hot water, the water inside expands.

hot water

water containing a dye

before   **after**

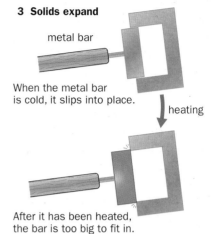

3 Solids expand

metal bar

When the metal bar is cold, it slips into place.

heating

After it has been heated, the bar is too big to fit in.

If you cool a solid, a liquid, or a gas, the opposite happens. They all **contract (get smaller)**.

When a metal bar is heated, its atoms get more energy. They move faster and bang into each other harder. This makes them move further apart, and so the whole bar expands slightly. When the metal cools down, the atoms lose energy. They move closer together, and the bar contracts again. The same thing happens for liquids and gases, but gases expand more than liquids, and liquids more than solids.

Effects of expansion and contraction

When solids, liquids, and gases expand and contract, they can produce very large forces. That can do real damage. Expansion in very hot summers has made railway lines bend, bridges buckle, and concrete pavements crack. Contraction in cold winters has snapped power cables.

Usually, however, it is possible to avoid this. Bridges, for example, have expansion joints built into them. This allows the bridges to expand and contract without damage. Power cables which are hung in summer are left slightly slack. When they contract in cold winters, they can become tighter without snapping.

Large slabs of concrete have expansion joints between them. These joints are made of tar. This is soft enough to be squashed by the slabs when they expand in hot weather.

1 *Water expands when it is heated and contracts when it is cooled*. What does this mean? ▲
2 Why does the metal bar expand when it is heated? ▲
3 Engineers who hang power cables from pylons in summer leave the cables slightly slack. Why? ▲

4 Why must oven shelves not fit tightly when the oven is cold?
5 Why should you never fill a pan of water right to the top if you are going to heat it?
6 **Try to find out**
  a how a thermometer works
  b why big slabs of concrete, e.g. on a motorway, are laid with tar between them.

DID YOU KNOW?
⟳ Gases expand roughly 3000 times more than solids.
⟳ The railway bridge over the River Forth in Scotland is made of steel and is about 2.5 km long. But it is 0.5 m longer in summer than in winter.

Floating and sinking can be puzzling. Why does a light copper coin sink when it is put in water? Why does a much heavier oak log float?

You will realize straight away that it can't be the mass of the object which makes it float or sink. What matters is its **density**. Wood floats because it has a smaller density than water. Copper sinks because its density is greater.

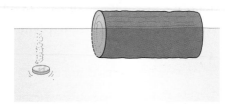

Why does this happen?

The density of a substance is the mass of 1 cm³ of it

Opposite, you can see the densities of some common substances. Can you see any patterns?

Why are some substances more dense than others?

The density of a substance depends on two things:
- the mass of the atoms (or molecules) which make it up
- how closely these atoms and molecules are packed together.

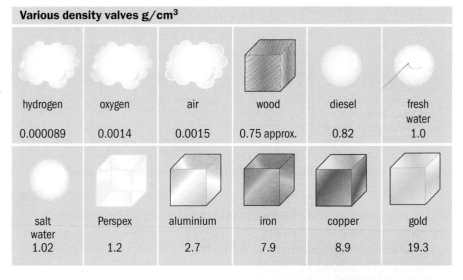

Various density valves g/cm³

hydrogen	oxygen	air	wood	diesel	fresh water
0.000089	0.0014	0.0015	0.75 approx.	0.82	1.0

salt water	Perspex	aluminium	iron	copper	gold
1.02	1.2	2.7	7.9	8.9	19.3

Gold is made up of heavy atoms packed closely together. A volume of 1 cm³ of gold has a big mass, and so gold has a high density. On the other hand, gases have very low densities. Gas molecules spread out to occupy a large volume, with lots of empty space. A volume of 1 cm³ of any gas is very light.

The density of a substance depends on its temperature. When you heat any substance, it expands. Its atoms and molecules move further apart and so it becomes less dense. That's why hot-air balloons rise. (Cold air is more dense so it pushes the warmer, less dense air out of the way (upwards).) The same effect happens with water. And that's why the water at the top of the hot-water tank at home is hottest.

Hot air has a different density from cold air. That's why hot-air balloons rise.

1 What is the density of a substance?
2 What does the density of a substance depend on? Why does gold have a large density?
3 Why does wood float on water while copper sinks? Would polythene float on paraffin? Explain your answer.
4 Why do bubbles rise when you open a bottle of lemonade?
5 Where would you expect the hottest air in a room to be? Why? (Ask for a thermometer to check your answer.)
6 **Try to find out** how a hot-air balloon works.

DID YOU KNOW?
- It's easier to float in the sea than in a lake. That's because sea water is denser than fresh water.
- The Dead Sea is so dense that you can float sitting up in it.

Here are some problems for you to think about. They are problems about expansion, pressure, and density. Work them out for yourself!

Pumping up a tyre

QUESTIONS

1 When you are pumping up a tyre
   a what are you pumping into the tyre?
   b what happens to the tyre?
   c why does this happen?
2 **Try to find out** how a tyre valve works.

Handle with care

with the subtle intrigue of a Designer Fragrance.
Caution: Do not use near fire or naked flame. Do not pierce or burn even after use. Do not spray eyes or face. Keep out of reach of young children.

An aerosol can will carry a warning not to heat it in case it catches fire or explodes.

QUESTIONS

1 What happens to the gas molecules inside the aerosol when the temperature rises?
2 What would happen if the temperature rose too high?
3 Why should you never put an aerosol can in a fire?

Safety first with glass

Heat does not pass through glass easily. That can cause problems.

QUESTIONS

1 Copy and complete. *You should never pour very hot water into a drinking glass. If you do, the glass on the inside will become _____ and will (expand/contract). The cold glass on the outside will _____. The whole glass may ____.*
2 Pyrex doesn't do this. **Try to find out** why not.

Checking the purity of gold

To find the density of a substance you divide its mass by its volume:

$$\text{density} = \frac{\text{mass}}{\text{volume}}$$

density 19.3 g/cm^3
gold

density 8.9 g/cm^3
copper

24 g ring volume 2.2 cm^3
9-carat gold

19 g ring volume 1.5 cm^3
18-carat gold

QUESTIONS

1 Work out the density of the metal in each ring.
2 Which ring has more copper in it? Explain.
3 A 24 carat gold ring has a density of 19.3 gm/cm^3. What does that tell you about it?
4 **Try to work out** what the number of carats tells you about a piece of gold.

Wherever the electricity is generated, distributing it around the country requires a huge network of cables that are all linked up. Whether they are above ground, like those here, or underground, the cables must be suitable for the voltages and currents that they carry. Insulating the cables from the ground – and people! – is, of course, essential. In this village, Glenview, in the Western Highlands, the residents are worried about the possible adverse health effects of the pylons and cables near their homes. The science and technology of electricity transmission and conduction on this scale is therefore quite complex. In this chapter, you will be introduced to some simpler electrical circuits, conductors, insulators, and resistors, and some of the different types of electrical circuits.

Electrical conductors allow electricity to pass.

Electrical insulators do not allow electricity to pass.

Materials usually fall into one of these two groups. The table of materials below shows a selection of materials:

Conductors	Insulators
metals, graphite (pencil lead), water, carbon	glass, rubber, wood, plastic, pure water, air

Good conductors, such as copper, are used when ease of electrical flow is needed: for example, conducting wires. Good insulators are used when electrical flow is not wanted: for example, surrounding conducting wires, in plugs, sockets, and switches, and in glass light bulbs.

Insulators are very important for safety in electrical work.

Testing for conductors and insulators

The circuit below can be used to test materials to see if they are conductors or insulators. The bulb is included to act as a signal to indicate that a current is flowing (or not).

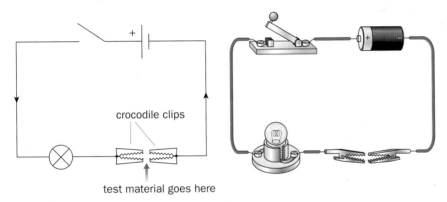

crocodile clips

test material goes here

If the test material is a conductor, then the lamp will light up when the switch is pressed.

Danger...!

Fishing near overhead electricity wires using a carbon fibre rod... pushing a screwdriver into a plug socket...using wet hands to touch anything electrical...handling wires with broken insulation: **all of these are dangerous and could kill you.**

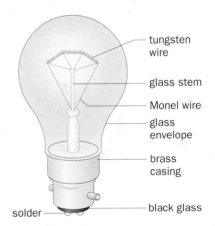

tungsten wire

glass stem

Monel wire

glass envelope

brass casing

black glass

solder

> **DID YOU KNOW?**
> ⊃ Impurities in water are responsible for making water a conductor. Unfortunately you will almost never come into contact with pure water (which is an insulator). So you should NEVER mix water and electricity!
> ⊃ Firefighters' helmets are made from insulators to protect them from bare electrical wires.

> **DID YOU KNOW?**
> ⊃ There is a third group of materials called semiconductors. They have special properties when it comes to allowing electricity to pass. Silicon and germanium are two examples. Semiconductors are used in 'chips' for computers.

QUESTIONS

1 What is a conductor? What is an insulator? ▲
2 List *two* conductors and *two* insulators of electricity. ▲
3 Why are plugs and switches made from plastic? ▲
4 A light bulb is made from a number of different materials. Which parts are conductors and which are insulators?
5 Look at the list of dangers. How many more can you think of?
6 **Try to find out** which metal is the best conductor.

You will use electrical circuits many times a day – even if you don't think about it. How often do you turn on the TV or radio, use the toaster, switch on a torch? You will have built simple devices in class – even if it was only a single bulb connected to a battery. Electrical 'bits and pieces' are the things you use when you make an electrical circuit.

Components and symbols

The bulbs, wires, batteries, and all the other things you use to make up a circuit are the 'bits and pieces', or components, of an electrical circuit.

Here is a selection of common components and their symbols:

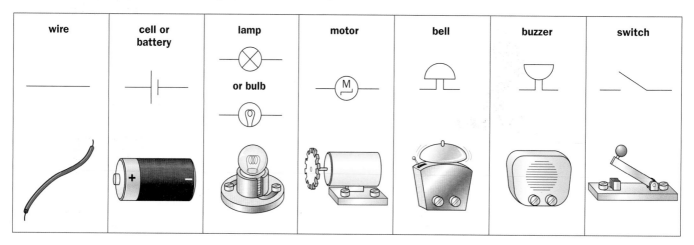

wire	cell or battery	lamp or bulb	motor	bell	buzzer	switch

Connections

When you assemble a selection of components, it is essential to connect them together well. Then the electricity will flow as easily as possible. Keep your connections bright and clean! This is especially so for copper wires, which can become dull.

Useful devices (are energy changers)

Usually you make an electric circuit to do something useful. You start with wires and a source of electricity, and then you add a bulb, a buzzer, or whatever you want to use. Many of these devices generate heat and get warm. Some also give out sound or light or both. They are energy changers. A lamp generates heat and light, a loudspeaker generates sound, movement, and heat. How many more examples can you think of?

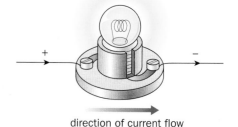

direction of current flow

When electricity travels (from positive to negative) through this bulb, energy is changed into light and heat.

1 What are the symbols for
   a a bulb? ▲
   b a motor? ▲
   c a buzzer? ▲
2 What does a switch do?
3 What is the main energy change in
   a a toaster?
   b a kettle?
   c a radio?
4 Why do you think symbols are used to draw circuits?
5 **Try to find out** about some more symbols for other simple circuit components.

Using different components you can build circuits to perform different functions. Here is a selection of simple circuits. You will see that all the components are arranged one after the other (we call this in series):

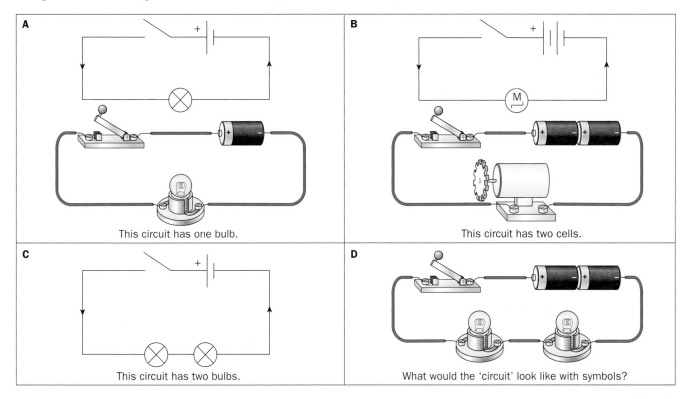

A This circuit has one bulb.

B This circuit has two cells.

C This circuit has two bulbs.

D What would the 'circuit' look like with symbols?

Does electricity disappear in a circuit?

You may have heard people say that electricity disappears. This is not true! When the electricity leaves the battery, it travels completely around the circuit and returns to the battery. You know this already because if a circuit is broken, the circuit will not work!

Direction of current flow

In three of the four circuits above (A, B, and C), arrows have been drawn to show which way the electrical current will flow when the circuits are switched on. For these circuits it is anticlockwise. The flow is from the positive terminal of the battery to the negative terminal of the batter. We say that current flows from positive to negative.

If you were to reverse the batteries, the current flow would reverse as well.

DiD YOU KNOW?

⮕ Circuits must be complete in order to work. If there any breaks in a circuit, it will not work.

1 List **all** the components used in each of the circuits A, B, C, and D above. ▲
2 How will the brightness of the bulbs in circuit C differ from the bulb in circuit A? ▲
3 Use symbols to draw circuit D. ▲

4 None of the circuits A–D are working. How will you show a working circuit using symbols? What will you have to change?
5 Using symbols, draw circuits containing
   a a buzzer and two batteries

b a lamp and two batteries. **Remember** to include a switch in each circuit.
6 Add direction arrows to the circuits you have drawn in Question 5 to show which way the current flows.

What's your favourite TV 'soap'? Whatever it is, you will know that one episode follows another, each week and every week. It just goes on and on...

A **series circuit** is rather like a TV soap. Each component follows the other: from one battery terminal around the circuit to the other terminal. All of the circuits you have met so far have been series circuits. The three circuits below are series circuits. You can follow them round with your finger – start at the positive terminal.

Some series go on and on and on...

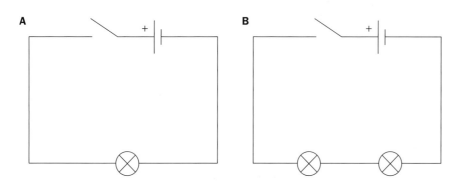

All bulbs are the same – what will be the differences between the circuits when they are switched on?

When the switches are closed, the single bulb shines most brightly, the three bulbs shine least brightly.

Changing the number of components

In two of the three circuits above (B and C), extra bulbs have been added. But only one battery is used in each. With one bulb in circuit A, all the electrical energy is available, so it shines most brightly. With three bulbs in circuit C to share the energy, each bulb's brightness is reduced.

If you were to replace the bulbs with, say, electric motors, then one would run faster and three would run more slowly.

Adding batteries has the opposite effect! One bulb with two batteries would shine more brightly than with one battery. The general series-circuit rule is: the more batteries the brighter, faster, noisier...

Warning

You have to match batteries with bulbs, motors, buzzers... If too much electricity is made to flow, then the other components may burn out – the circuit will be 'broken', and the circuit will stop working.

1. What is special about the components in a series circuit?
2. To make circuit A you would need six separate components. How many would you need for circuits B and C?
3. If one of the bulbs in circuit B 'blows', what will happen to the other bulb?
4. Naswan replaces the single battery in circuit B with two batteries of the same type. He expects the bulbs to glow more brightly. But they both go dimmer. Suggest a reason why.
5. In circuit C, how would you make the three bulbs shine as brightly as the bulb in circuit A?

Going further

You will have driven down busy roads that have more than one lane of traffic in each direction. Many motorways have two or three lanes in each direction. In each direction all the traffic lanes travel parallel to one another.

There is a similar idea in electric circuits where more than one pathway is provided for the electricity to flow. This is the **parallel circuit**.

The diagram shows a series circuit and then how it has been modified with a section containing two pathways – the parallel part. The circuit is then called a parallel circuit.

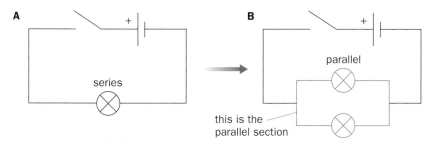

When these circuits are switched on, the brightness of all bulbs is the same.

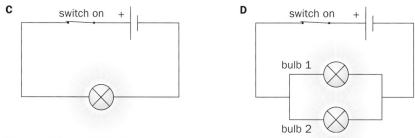

The parallel circuit (D) allows the same current to flow in each branch. So the bulbs are equally bright.

Advantage of parallel circuits

The branches or pathways in a parallel section are independent. So if one fails, any others are not affected. In circuit D, above, if either of the two bulbs fails, the remaining bulb is completely unaffected and will stay bright.

Independence

It is possible to treat each branch completely independently by adding a switch into each of them. The diagram below shows this for two and three bulbs connected in parallel.

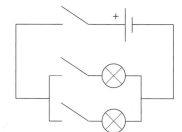

Two bulbs and two switches

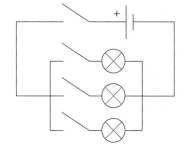

Three bulbs and three switches

1 Rewrite the following sentences by leaving out the incorrect word choices:
   *In a **parallel** circuit many bulbs can be connected in **the same/different branch/branches.** All bulbs will have **the same/different** brightness.*

2 In circuit D, both bulbs are of equal brightness. What do you think happens to the current at the junctions of the two parallel branches?

3 Draw a circuit with three bulbs. One bulb must remain on all the time and the other two must be independent.

4 What advantages do parallel circuits have when compared with series circuits?

The diagram below shows part of a parallel circuit. Electricity arrives at and leaves from the circuit through the wires on the left. Then there are devices connected in parallel. They could be bulbs, motors, radios, or any other device that works by electricity.

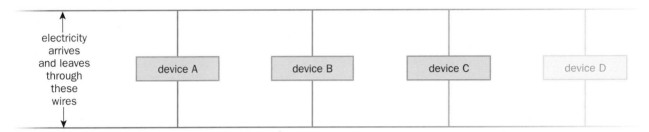

electricity arrives and leaves through these wires

The devices (A, B, and C) could be anything you have in your home:
your hifi, radio, TV, microwave, lamps, washing machine…

If for any reason one of the devices stops working, it will have no effect on the others.

Extending the circuit into a ring

You can extend a parallel circuit for as long as you like, or, in other words, you can go on adding more devices on the end. The diagram below has been rearranged into a ring. This is known as the **household ring main**. In practice, it allows you to plug in many devices around the home.

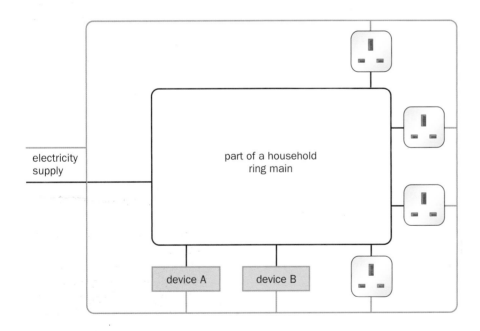

electricity supply

part of a household ring main

device A   device B

DiD YOU KNOW?
⟹ WARNING: NEVER PLAY WITH ELECTRICITY FROM THE MAINS. IT IS LIKELY TO KILL YOU!

1 Make up a set of rules for the safe use of electrical devices/sockets.
2 There are a number of separate ring mains in your home. Ask an adult to help and **try to find out** how many there are and what each is used for.

The amount of electricity flowing in a circuit can be measured. The device used to make this measurement of 'how much' is the ammeter. An ammeter and its circuit symbol are shown on the right.

Units of current flow
Current flow is measured in **amperes**. It should be written 'amperes' but sometimes is written 'amps'. The symbol, which is more usually used, is a capital 'A'. So, 1 A is a current flow of one ampere...and so on.

Connecting ammeters
In the same way that you connect any device into a circuit, the ammeter plugs in with connectors. An ammeter has two connectors. One is labelled positive (+ve) and one is labelled negative (–ve). Unlike with many devices, it is absolutely vital to place ammeters the right way round. Ammeters are always connected in series.

Ammeters in circuits
The diagrams below show how an ammeter can be placed (in series) in a circuit.

An ammeter and its symbol.

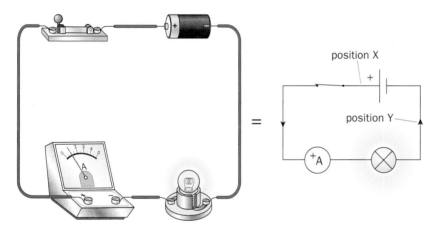

Current flow around a series circuit is constant, so you can place the ammeter in any position. It could go before the switch in position X or after the bulb in position Y. The ammeter readings would be the same.

> **DiD YOU KNOW?**
> ➲ Whatever current flows into a device always flows out again.

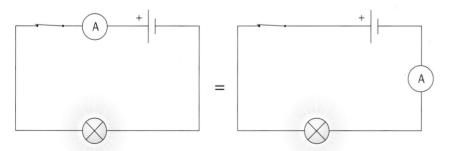

These arrangements will also measure the current correctly. Remember to keep the positive connection of the ammeter leading to the positive battery terminal.

QUESTIONS

1 What is the unit of current flow? ▲
2 What device measures current flow? ▲
3 If you place an ammeter in different positions around a series circuit, will the measurements be the same or different? ▲
4 If a current of 3 A flows into a bulb, how much current flows out of the bulb? ▲

In all the circuits you have seen, you have thought about current flow. But something has to 'force' the current to flow. It doesn't flow on its own. The driving force of a current is called **voltage**. The unit is the **volt**, and it has the symbol capital 'V'. Batteries are labelled with voltage values. You will recognize some of these voltage values: 1.5 V, 3 V, 230 V.

Changing the driving force

Voltage values give you an idea of the strength of the driving force. If you double the driving force (from, say, 1.5 V to 3 V) then you will double the current flowing. If you halve the driving force in a circuit (from, say, 12 V to 6 V), then the current flowing will halve.

If you add extra batteries in series to a circuit, the voltages add together.

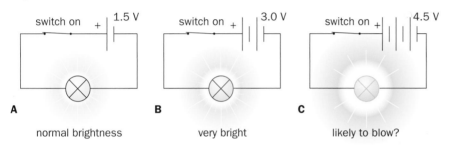

A normal brightness   **B** very bright   **C** likely to blow?

As the voltage increases, the 'driving force' will drive more current around the circuit – in turn, the bulb will glow more brightly (and may blow). It is important to match the voltage values of components in a circuit.

Voltmeters: voltage measurers

Voltage is measured using a voltmeter. But, unlike with an ammeter, you make a measurement where you want to measure what is flowing constantly through the meter. Voltage is a measurement of difference. This is because you are measuring a 'driving force' and the force will be greatest at the beginning and zero at the end. For this reason you 'dip in' with the voltmeter connections as if you were creating a connection in parallel. The diagrams below show how you make measurements.

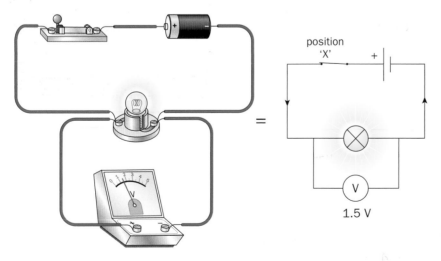

This voltmeter is connected in parallel with the bulb. It will measure the current's driving force from one side of the bulb to the other.

Questions

1. What is the unit of voltage? ▲
2. You add three batteries in series. Each battery is marked 1.5 V. What is the total voltage value of the combined battery? ▲
3. In the three circuits A, B, and C, what voltage values should the three bulbs have?
4. You find three batteries marked 1.5 V, 3 V, and 6 V. What are all the different voltages you can supply?
5. You have three batteries marked 1.5 V. When you connect them in series and measure the total voltage with a voltmeter the reading is only 1.5 V. You were expecting 4.5 V. What could have gone wrong?

A voltmeter and its symbol.

DID YOU KNOW?

➔ A 'driving force' or voltage of less than 80 volts is enough to kill you. This is much less than the voltage of the mains electricity used in the home (230 V).

At some time or other you will have seen a blown bulb. Perhaps you have made one blow by connecting it to a voltage that is too high!

A bulb filament blows usually because it has become too hot – it may melt and may burn. Whatever the reason, the connection breaks and the circuit stops working.

Materials and their resistance

All materials have a resistance to the flow of electricity through them. Some have a higher resistance than others. A current flowing through a resistance wire causes a heating effect – too great, and it melts or burns and blows.

You can show this heating effect by using some fine pieces of steel wool in a circuit and gradually increasing the current flow through them.

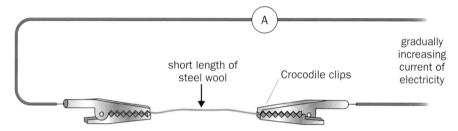

short length of steel wool

Crocodile clips

gradually increasing current of electricity

As the current through the steel wire increases, the wire heats up. After a while, the wire will glow, and the results may be quite 'sparkling'!

Fuses and the resistance–heating effect

The **resistance–heating effect** can be put to good use. A piece of specially chosen wire can be added to a circuit so that it melts first – before the connecting wires do. This fuse wire has a low melting point, and when it heats up beyond a certain temperature, it melts and cuts off the supply of electricity.

Fuses can be made of different thicknessness of wire to suit different applications. They are labelled or rated in amperes. A 5 ampere (5 A) fuse will only allow a current of about 5 A to flow through it before it melts. Fuses are vital for the safe operation of devices connected to mains electricity.

DiD YOU KNOW?
➲ Common values for fuses are 3 A, 5 A, and 13 A.

QUESTIONS

1 Give *two* reasons a bulb might blow. ▲
2 **a** If a material conducts electricity easily, it will have a _____ _____. ▲
   b If a material does not conduct electricity easily, it will have a _____ _____. ▲
3 A current flowing through a resistance will cause a _____ _____. ▲
4 What are two common fuse values? ▲
5 If you use a fuse in a circuit that has too low a value, what will happen? If you use a fuse that has too high a value, what will happen?

1 Work out the missing values for current and voltage in the four sets of circuits (A, B, C, and D).
2 Some of the bulbs blow and go out. These bulbs are marked with an X. What effect do these blown bulbs have on the voltage and current values?

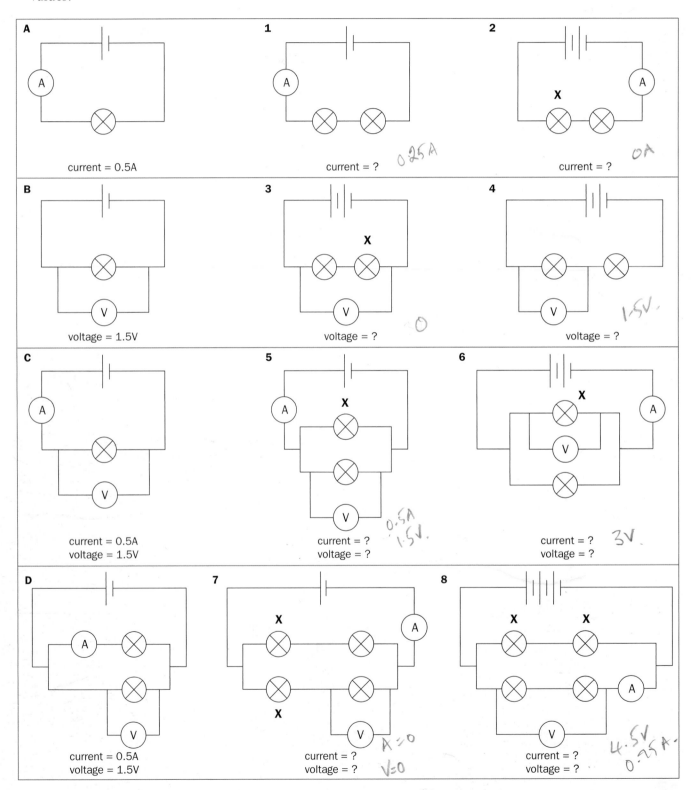

A
current = 0.5A

1
current = ? 0.25A

2
current = ? 0A

B
voltage = 1.5V

3
voltage = ? 0

4
voltage = ? 1.5V.

C
current = 0.5A
voltage = 1.5V

5
current = ? 0.5A
voltage = ? 1.5V.

6
current = ? 3V.
voltage = ?

D
current = 0.5A
voltage = 1.5V

7
current = ? A = 0
voltage = ? V = 0

8
current = ? 4.5V
voltage = ? 0.25A.

Meet Morag, the sheep. She was one of the first sheep to be cloned from embryo cells, in 1995. (You can now see her as a permanent exhibit at the Royal Museum, Edinburgh.) As a result of their work with Morag and her twin sister Megan, in 1996 scientists at the Roslin Institute near Edinburgh cloned Dolly, who must be the most famous sheep in the world! They were successful where others had failed for several decades because Dolly is the first adult mammal to be successfully cloned from the genetic material in the cell of another adult, rather than being the result of natural reproduction. To be able to do this, natural reproduction had first to be fully understood. This chapter introduces the natural processes of reproduction in animals (including humans) and plants.

All animals and plants are made up of 'building blocks' called cells.
Most animals and plants are made up of millions of cells joined together.
Animal and plant cells have similar jobs to do. They take in food, release
energy, get rid of waste, grow; and reproduce.

Animal cell: cheek

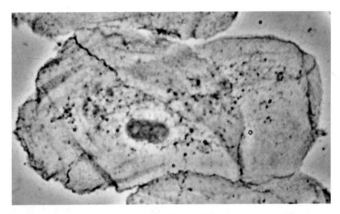

This is a photo of a cheek cell. The inside of your cheek is made
up of many of these cells. In fact, your whole body is made up of
millions and millions of tiny living cells joined together.

A diagram to help you see the main parts of the cheek
cell is given below:

The nucleus is the 'control centre' of the cell. The nucleus contains the information which controls everything which goes on in the cell.

The cytoplasm is all the living matter, except for the nucleus. It is a jelly-like substance which is fluid (it can flow).

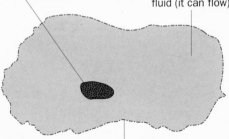

The cell membrane is a thin skin round the outside of the cell.
It prevents the cell material from escaping. But it does allow
substances like food and oxygen to cross in and out of the cell.

Plant cell: pond weed

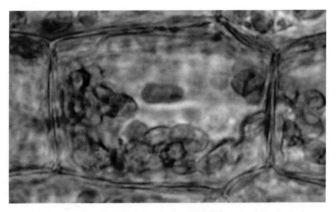

This is a photo of a cell from pond weed. The weed is made up
of millions of tiny living cells, too.

A diagram to help you see the main parts of the pond
weed cell is given below:

The cell wall is a rigid (firm) coating round the outside of the cell. It helps the plant cell to keep its shape.

nucleus

The cell membrane is inside the cell wall.

cytoplasm

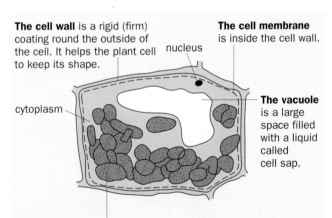

The vacuole is a large space filled with a liquid called cell sap.

Chloroplasts contain the green chemical called
chlorophyll. This is the chemical which allows green
plants to use the Sun's light energy.

---

1 Why is the nucleus called the 'control centre' of the cell? ▲
2 What is the cytoplasm? What is it like? ▲
3 What is a cell vacuole? ▲
4 a What do chloroplasts contain?
  b Why is this important? ▲

5 Pick out the *three* parts which are found both in the cheek cell and in the pond weed cell (and in most other cells, too!). ▲
6 **Try to find out** when cells were discovered, and by whom.

Cells and tissue

Animals and plants are made up of lots of different types of cell. Each type carries out a different job. Cells that do the same job join together to make **tissue**.

Muscle cells, for example, join together to make tissue that can contract and relax.

Meat is mainly muscle tissue.

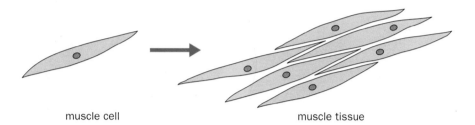

muscle cell　　　　　　　muscle tissue

Organs

Different tissue joins together to make an **organ**.

The stomach is an organ that digests food. Muscle tissue, nerve tissue, and blood tissue are just some of the types of tissue that make up the stomach.

This pine tree by Loch Maree is an **organism**. All organisms are made up of many different organs.

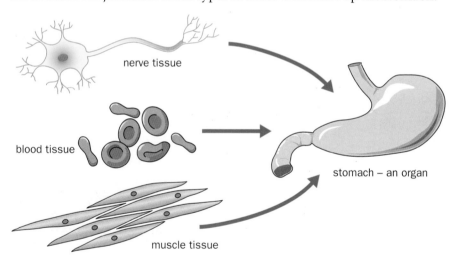

nerve tissue

blood tissue

stomach – an organ

muscle tissue

---

1 **a** What is tissue?
  b Name *three* types of tissue. ▲
2 **a** Name an organ found in the human body.
  b List *three* types of tissue that make up this organ. ▲
3 Put these words in the right order starting with the simplest:
  organ cell organism tissue ▲

4 Explain the difference between an organ and an organism.
5 The brain is another organ in the human body. Suggest what types of tissue make up the brain.
6 **Try to find out** the name of one organ that is part of a pine tree.

DiD YOU KNOW?
➲ There are three kinds of muscle tissue. Each type has a different job to do.
➲ Muscle tissue makes up about 40% of a mammal's weight.

There are many different kinds of animal and plant cells. Each one is suited to the job it has to do. The photographs show a few of these different cells – there are lots more.

In animals there are...

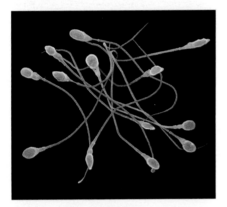

...sperm cells, which have a streamlined shape. This helps them swim through the fluid in the female reproductive system to fertilize an egg.

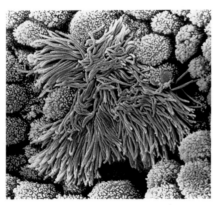

...cells with tiny hairs (called **cilia**), which move liquid over the surface of the windpipe/lungs to keep them clean.

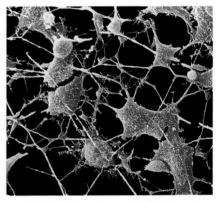

...nerve cells, which have long, thin fibres that carry messages from one part of the body to another.

In plants there are...

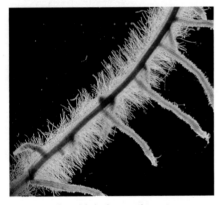

...root cells with hairs on them to increase surface area and so take up more water from the soil.

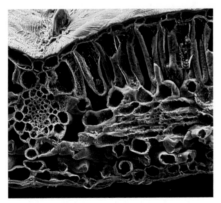

...cells in leaves which are full of chloroplasts to absorb sunlight for photosynthesis.

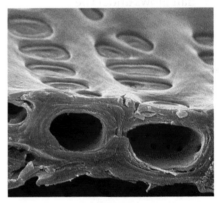

...cells in the stem which have extra thickening in their walls to provide support.

1 Describe how
  a a sperm cell
  b a nerve cell
  c root hair cells
  d stem cells
  are suited to their jobs. ▲
2 Why do cells lining the lungs have tiny cilia on them? ▲

3 How are leaves adapted for photosynthesis? ▲
4 Why do you think there are so many types of cells in complex animals like humans?
5 **Try to find out** how red blood cells are suited to their job of carrying oxygen around the body.

DiD YOU KNOW?

➲ A frog's skin has cells which contain a coloured pigment. The pigment can be concentrated or spread out to change the colour of the skin from brown to green and back again.

Humans, like most animals, reproduce by producing special cells called **sex cells**. This is why the process is called **sexual reproduction**.

Before a boy and a girl can have children of their own they must become sexually mature.

The time when this happens is called **puberty**.

Puberty usually starts at the age of 11–13 in girls and about 12–14 in boys. People vary a lot, so there is nothing wrong with you if puberty comes earlier or later in your life.

DID YOU KNOW?
➲ In China, children appear to reach puberty a year earlier than in Europe. This is because the Chinese consider a baby to be one year old on the day it is born.

What happens at puberty?
During puberty we grow fast and develop **secondary sexual characteristics**.

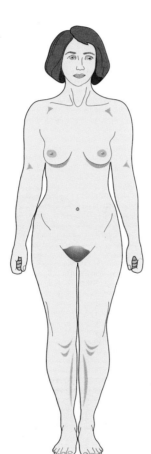

Secondary sexual characteristics in women:
➲ breasts develop
➲ hips get bigger
➲ hair grows under the arms and around the vagina
➲ ovaries start producing **eggs** (female sex cells)
➲ periods start – this is called **menstruation**. Menstruation happens about once a month.

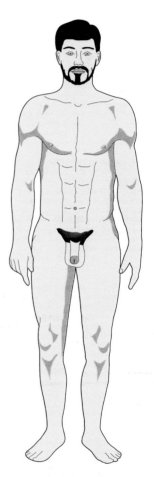

Secondary sexual characteristics in men:
➲ voice gets deeper
➲ body becomes more muscular
➲ hair grows on the face and body
➲ testes start producing **sperm** (male sex cells) – sometimes sperm pass from the body at night. These 'wet dreams' are natural and quite harmless.

1 Why is reproduction in humans called sexual reproduction? ▲
2 What is puberty? ▲
3 Roughly, when does puberty happen
  a in girls?   **b** in boys? ▲

4 Describe the changes that happen at puberty in the body of
  a a girl   **b** a boy. ▲

5 Explain why girls can sing high notes all through their lives but boys can't after the age of about 14.
6 **Try to find out** how long it takes a mouse to reach puberty.

Male and female sex cells are produced in parts of the body called **sex organs**.

The male has **testes** which produce the sperm. The female has **ovaries** which produce the eggs.

Male sex organs

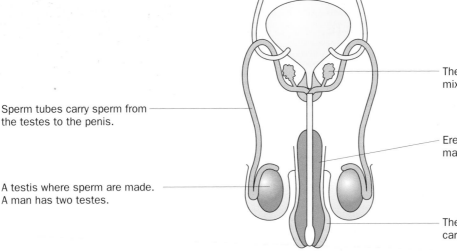

Sperm tubes carry sperm from the testes to the penis.

A testis where sperm are made. A man has two testes.

These glands make a liquid that mixes with the sperm.

Erectile tissue fills with blood to make the penis hard and erect.

The **penis** is put inside the vagina and carries sperm during mating.

Female sex organs

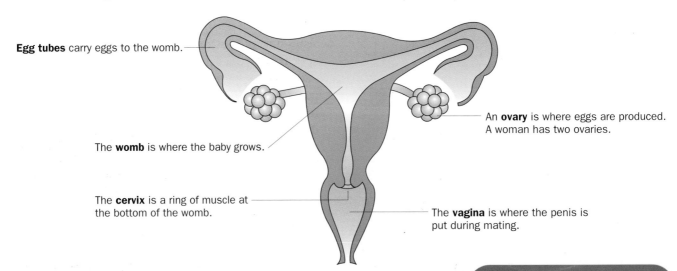

Egg tubes carry eggs to the womb.

The **womb** is where the baby grows.

The **cervix** is a ring of muscle at the bottom of the womb.

An **ovary** is where eggs are produced. A woman has two ovaries.

The **vagina** is where the penis is put during mating.

1. What are produced in sex organs? ▲
2. What are male sex cells called? Where are they reproduced? ▲
3. What are female sex cells called? Where are they produced? ▲
4. Why does the penis have erectile tissue in it? ▲
5. **Try to find out** the job of the liquid produced by the glands in the male reproductive organs.

DID YOU KNOW?

- A human egg is about this size → .
- Sperm are much smaller.
- A woman will produce between 300 and 500 eggs in her lifetime.
- A man will produce billions of sperm during his life.

An egg is fertilized when the nucleus of one sperm joins with the egg nucleus.

Sexual intercourse

If a sperm is to meet an egg, **sexual intercourse** must happen. When a man gets sexually excited he gets an **erection**. Blood flows into the erectile tissue in the penis and makes it hard. The man moves his penis up and down inside the woman's vagina. After a while fluid containing sperm is pumped from the testes through his penis into the woman's body. This is called an **ejaculation**. The man feels a good sensation (an **orgasm**) when he ejaculates. A woman may also have an orgasm during intercourse.

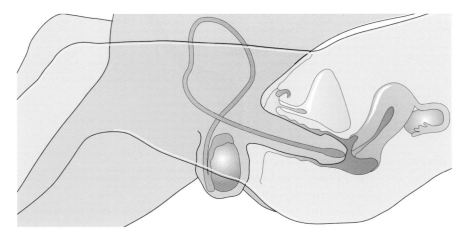

Fertilization

After being ejaculated, sperm swim through the womb and into the egg tubes. If a sperm meets an egg, fertilization happens. The fertilized egg travels down the egg tube and becomes fixed in the newly prepared lining of the womb.

> ## DiD YOU KNOW?
> ⊃ A sperm's tail lashes like a whip. This is how the sperm moves forward.
> ⊃ A healthy human male will release between 300 to 400 million sperm in one ejaculation. However, only about 100 will reach the egg and only **one** will fertilize it.

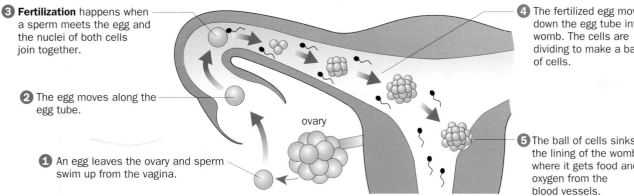

❸ **Fertilization** happens when a sperm meets the egg and the nuclei of both cells join together.

❷ The egg moves along the egg tube.

❶ An egg leaves the ovary and sperm swim up from the vagina.

ovary

❹ The fertilized egg moves down the egg tube into the womb. The cells are dividing to make a ball of cells.

❺ The ball of cells sinks into the lining of the womb where it gets food and oxygen from the blood vessels.

---

1 What is sexual intercourse? ▲

2 a Explain how an erection happens.
  b Why is an erection important?

3 What is
  a an ejaculation?
  b an orgasm? ▲

4 Where does fertilization happen? ▲

5 Describe what happens to an egg after it is fertilized. ▲

6 **Try to find out** how fast sperm can swim.

Pregnancy

During **pregnancy** the ball of cells in the womb lining slowly grows into tissues and organs. During the next 9 months the developing baby grows from a single cell to a baby half a metre long and weighing about 3 kg.

The developing baby (**embryo**) is warm and well protected. It grows in a bag (the **amnion**) of watery liquid (**amniotic fluid**) which acts like a cushion. A flexible tube called the **umbilical cord** connects the embryo to the **placenta**. Food and oxygen cross from the mother's blood to the baby's blood in the placenta. The diagram shows how this happens.

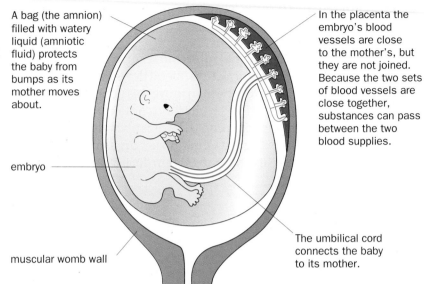

A bag (the amnion) filled with watery liquid (amniotic fluid) protects the baby from bumps as its mother moves about.

In the placenta the embryo's blood vessels are close to the mother's, but they are not joined. Because the two sets of blood vessels are close together, substances can pass between the two blood supplies.

embryo

The umbilical cord connects the baby to its mother.

muscular womb wall

Birth

A few weeks before birth, the baby turns upside down so its head lies just above the cervix. When the baby is ready to be born, the mother 'goes into labour'. The muscles in the womb wall contract slowly at first, then quicker and stronger. These contractions burst the amnion, releasing the fluid. The cervix relaxes to let the baby's head through.

The mother uses her tummy muscles to help the muscles in her womb to push the baby out into the world. The umbilical cord is tied and cut.

A few minutes after the baby is born, the womb muscles push the placenta and remains of the umbilical cord out of the womb. These are the **afterbirth**.

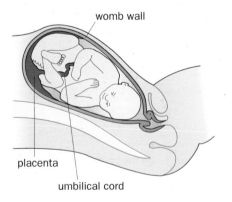

womb wall

placenta

umbilical cord

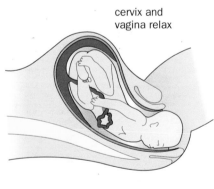

cervix and vagina relax

During its first months the baby will get all the food it needs from its mother. It suckles milk from **mammary glands** inside its mother's breasts.

1 **a** How long does pregnancy take in humans?
  b How big is a human baby when it is born? ▲
2 What is the job of the bag of amniotic fluid? ▲
3 **a** Why does the growing embryo depend on the umbilical cord? ▲
  b Why can the cord be cut safely after the baby is born? ▲
4 Describe how a baby is born.
5 **Try to find out** what special foods a pregnant woman should eat.

DID YOU KNOW?
➲ A pregnant woman shouldn't drink alcohol, smoke, or take drugs unless given by a doctor. All of these can seriously affect the development of the baby.

A woman will produce hundreds of eggs in her lifetime. Only a few, if any, will ever be fertilized, either because she hasn't had sexual intercourse, or she has, but it happened when there was no egg present in an egg tube.

Eggs only live for about 2 days. When an egg isn't fertilized, the thickened lining of the womb breaks down. Unwanted cells and blood are pushed from the womb through the vagina. This is a **period** or **menstruation**. Periods last for about five days and can cause some discomfort. This is because the contractions of the womb cause pains – a bit like cramp.

Monthly changes

Periods are just one of the changes that happen in a woman's body every 28 days or so. They are part of the **menstrual cycle**. The diagram shows the four stages in the cycle.

Women wear sanitary towels or tampons to absorb the blood lost in menstruation. These must be changed regularly.

Stage 4: The womb lining stays thick for about 14 days. If an egg is not fertilized on day 28, the womb lining will break down again, starting another period.

Stage 1: On day 1 the lining of the womb starts to break down and blood comes out of the vagina. This is called **menstruation** or a **period** and it lasts for about 5 days.

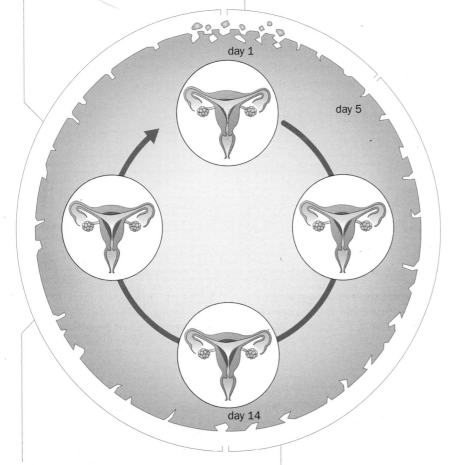

day 1

day 5

day 14

Stage 3: On day 14 an egg is produced from an ovary. This is called **ovulation**. The woman is now fertile. If mating happens now she could become **pregnant**.

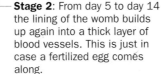

egg

Stage 2: From day 5 to day 14 the lining of the womb builds up again into a thick layer of blood vessels. This is just in case a fertilized egg comes along.

DID YOU KNOW?

➲ Many women get depressed and irritable during the days before a period. This is often called pre-menstrual tension (PMT) or pre-menstrual syndrome (PMS).

1 a What is another name for a period?
  b Describe what happens during a period. ▲
2 a How long does the menstrual cycle usually take?
  b How many stages are there in the menstrual cycle? ▲
3 a Explain why women wear sanitary towels or tampons.
  b Why is it important to change these regularly? ▲
4 Why do you think menstruation stops when a woman is pregnant?
5 If a woman wants to avoid getting pregnant, when should she not have sexual intercourse? (**Hint**: Sperm live for about five days.)
6 **Try to find out** the scientific name for the lining of the womb.

It's hard to believe that a cell's nucleus contains all the instructions needed for the cell to do its work. It's even harder to believe that the nucleus of a fertilized egg contains all the instructions needed for a new animal to grow. But it does – and the passing on of these instructions is all-important.

Chromosomes

The instructions are carried on fine threads of material called **chromosomes**. Every cell in the animal's body, apart from sperm and egg cells, has the same number and kind of chromosomes in its nucleus. Human cells have 46 chromosomes, horse cells have 60, mouse cells have 40, and so on. Sperm and eggs have only half that number. When a sperm and an egg join up, a new animal begins to grow. Fertilization is really the putting together of a 'full set' of instructions needed for the animal to grow. Half of the instructions are passed on from the father, in the sperm, half from the mother, in the egg.

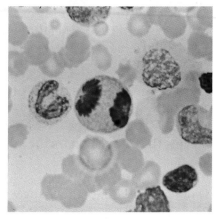
Chromosomes dividing in human cells

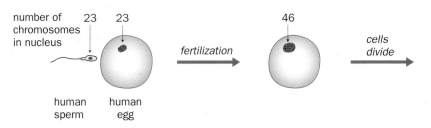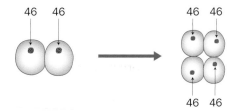

As more and more cells are produced and the animal develops, the same instructions are passed on from one cell to the next. This is how each cell gets the same set of chromosomes when a cell divides. To make things simpler, only four chromosomes are shown in the diagram. There are three main stages:

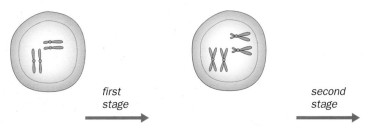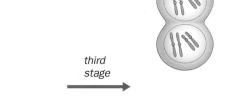

1 Each chromosome makes an exact copy of itself.

2 The copies separate. One chromosome from each pair goes to one side of the cell, the other to the opposite side.

3 The cell divides. New nuclei form. Each daughter cell has the same chromosomes as the parent.

---

1 What is a chromosome? Where are chromosomes found? Why are they important? ▲

2 How many chromosomes are there in the nucleus of
  a a human skin cell?
  b a horse sperm cell?
  c a mouse egg cell?

3 When a human egg is fertilized:
23 + 23 = 46
When a human cell divides:
46 → 92 → 46 + 46
In each case, explain what is meant.

4 **Try to find out** what the 'instructions' on a chromosome are called.

DiD YOU KNOW?

➲ A chromosome is only about 0.005 mm long.

➲ Scientists are now able to change some of the chromosome material in a nucleus.

Whether you are naturally tall or small, blond- or brown-haired, blue- or green-eyed, left- or right-handed depends largely on the **genes** in your body cells. A gene is part of one of the chromosome threads inside the nucleus of each cell. Genes control the characteristics which are passed on from parents to their children.

When an egg is fertilized, two sets of genes are put together. One set comes from the father in the sperm's chromosomes. The other set, from the mother, is in the egg's chromosomes. Each set carries half of the total instructions for the new human.

The two sets of genes in a fertilized egg are very similar. The genes passed on by the father, for example, carry instructions about body characteristics like height, hair colour, and eye colour. The genes passed on by the mother carry instructions about these characteristics too.

Dominant and recessive gene alleles

The genes in a pair may carry the same message. Both parents may pass on a gene for brown hair to their child and so the child will have brown hair.

But sometimes one of the genes carries a different message from the other. These are called **gene alleles** – different forms of the gene. For example, a person has two alleles for hair colour (one pair). One allele says 'have blond hair', the other allele says 'have black hair'. These alleles are in competition with each other.

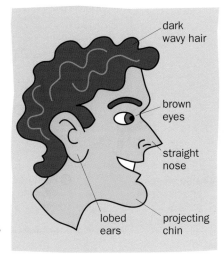

dark wavy hair

brown eyes

straight nose

lobed ears

projecting chin

Other dominant characteristics

The person with these alleles will have black hair, because the allele for black hair is more powerful than the allele for blond hair. The allele for black hair is **dominant** and produces the final hair colour. The allele for blond hair is **recessive**. Whenever a dominant allele pairs up with a recessive allele, the dominant allele produces the final effect.

DID YOU KNOW?

➲ You can't teach yourself how to roll your tongue. Whether you are a tongue roller or not depends on the genes you have inherited!

➲ Sometimes, the ball of cells which grows from the fertilized egg splits into two. Each half grows into a baby. That's how identical twins are produced, and that's why identical twins have identical genes.

1 **a** What is a gene?
  b What do genes do? ▲
2 List *three* examples of characteristics that are controlled by genes. ▲
3 How are genes passed from parents to their children? ▲
4 **a** What is a gene allele?
  b Give an example of an allele. ▲

5 Explain the difference between a dominant and a recessive gene allele.
6 A sperm carrying an allele for lobed ears fertilizes an egg carrying an allele for non-lobed ears.
  a What sort of ears will the child have?
  b Explain your answer.

Every part of a plant has its own special job to do. The flower's job is to allow the plant to reproduce by sexual reproduction. It produces the male sex cells (which are contained in pollen grains) and the female sex cells (contained in the ovules).

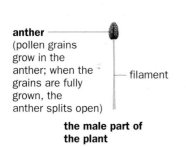

anther
(pollen grains grow in the anther; when the grains are fully grown, the anther splits open)

filament

the male part of the plant

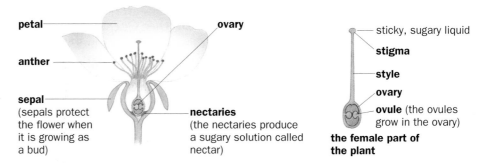

petal

ovary

anther

sepal
(sepals protect the flower when it is growing as a bud)

nectaries
(the nectaries produce a sugary solution called nectar)

sticky, sugary liquid

stigma

style

ovary

ovule (the ovules grow in the ovary)

the female part of the plant

Pollination

The first step in reproduction is **pollination**. A flower is pollinated when a pollen grain lands on its stigma.

The pollen grain can be carried from an anther to the stigma of the same flower (self-pollination). Or it can be carried to the stigma of another flower (**cross-pollination**). Some flowers' pollen is carried by insects. Other flowers' pollen is carried by the wind.

Pollination must be followed by **fertilization**. The male sex cells must join up with the female sex cells before a new plant can grow.

The diagrams opposite show how pollination and fertilization take place in an insect-pollinated flower.

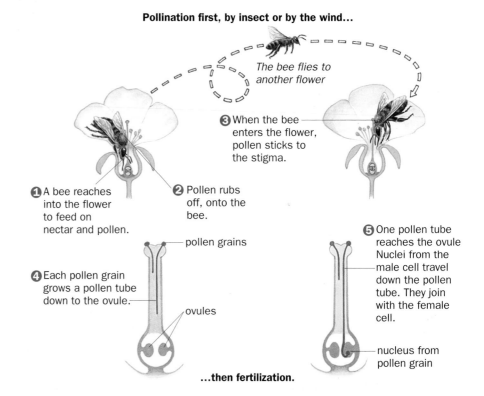

Pollination first, by insect or by the wind...

The bee flies to another flower

❸ When the bee enters the flower, pollen sticks to the stigma.

❶ A bee reaches into the flower to feed on nectar and pollen.

❷ Pollen rubs off, onto the bee.

pollen grains

❹ Each pollen grain grows a pollen tube down to the ovule.

ovules

❺ One pollen tube reaches the ovule Nuclei from the male cell travel down the pollen tube. They join with the female cell.

nucleus from pollen grain

...then fertilization.

1 Why are
  a sepals
  b anthers
  c ovaries
  important to a flower? ▲

2 What happens in
  a pollination?
  b fertilization? ▲

3 Is the flower in the five-stage diagram above being self-pollinated or cross-pollinated? Explain your answer.

4 How can pollen be carried from flower to flower? ▲

5 Pollen grain **A** is small and very light. Pollen grain **B** is sticky. One is pollen from a buttercup. The other is pollen from a grass. Say which is which, giving reasons for your answer.

DiD YOU KNOW?

➲ Bright flowers are usually insect-pollinated. Grass flowers are mostly wind-pollinated.

➲ If a pollen grain lands on the stigma of another kind of flower, the pollen grain dies.

After the ovules have been fertilized, most of the flower withers and dies. At the same time, the fertilized ovules grow inside the ovary until they develop into seeds. Each seed contains a tiny embryo plant. It also contains a food store. Round the seed is a tough **seed coat** which protects it.

The ovary grows, too. The developed ovary, with the seeds inside it, is called a **fruit**. A pea pod, a plum, and a sycamore propeller are all fruits.

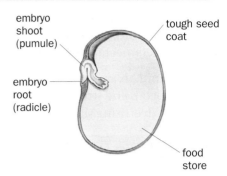

embryo shoot (pumule)

tough seed coat

embryo root (radicle)

food store

A broad bean seed (cut across)

Scattering the seeds

In many plants, the seeds are scattered. Often the whole fruit is scattered, with the seed inside. This scattering is important. Plants which are overcrowded don't grow well. Scattering gives the plants more room to grow.

dandelion fruit

sycamore fruit

'Parachute' and 'propellers' catch the wind.

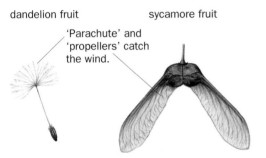

Some seeds are scattered by the wind.

burdock fruit

cherry

Seeds are left behind in animal droppings.

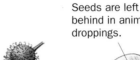

Hooks catch on animals' coats.

Some seeds are scattered by animals.

sweet pea

On a hot day, when the pod is dry, it bursts open. This scatters the seed.

Some seeds are scattered by explosions.

Germination

If the conditions are right, a seed will begin to grow or **germinate**. The seed which is scattered from the plant has very little water in it. A new plant begins to grow when the seed takes in water.

new leaves

new root

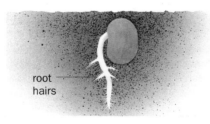

root hairs

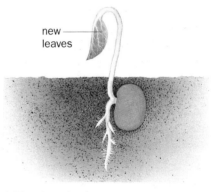

1 When the bean seed takes in water, the root begins to grow, using the stored food for energy.

2 The root continues to grow. The root hairs begin to take in water from the soil.

3 The shoot begins to grow. Then leaves appear.

1 What happens to
  a the flower **b** the ovule
  c the ovary wall
  after fertilization takes place? ▲
2 a Give one reason why it is better for seeds to be scattered from the plant.
  b Give *three* ways in which seeds are scattered. ▲

3 What happens when a seed germinates? Where does the growing embryo get its energy from?
4 Seeds don't germinate in the packet. Why is this?
5 Try to find out about other seeds and how they are scattered.

DID YOU KNOW?

➲ A strawberry isn't a real fruit. The fruits are the 'pips' on the outside.

➲ In 1954, 10 000-year-old seeds were found in frozen ground in Canada. In 1966, they germinated!

Insects are the only animals which pollinate European flowers. But in other parts of the world, some flowers are pollinated by birds and bats which feed on the flowers' nectar and pollen in the same way that insects do.

All these animals are attracted by the flowers' 'advertising signs' – brightly coloured petals and strong scents. But different animals are attracted to different 'advertising signs', sometimes for the strangest reasons.

Birds can see red well. Bird-pollinated flowers are usually bright red, or orange, or scarlet.

Insects are attracted to most colours, but only butterflies and moths can see the red colour which we see.

Many flowers have coloured stripes called 'honey guides' on their petals. Once the animal arrives on the flower, the stripes guide it to the nectar.

Most insects are attracted to sweet-smelling flowers. It is thought that the scents remind them of their food.

Carrion flowers are anything but sweet-smelling! They smell and look like rotting flesh. They are pollinated by insects which lay their eggs on dead flesh.

This orchid has such a strong scent that it makes any visiting bee 'drunk'. The bee falls into the flower. The only way it can escape is past the orchid's anthers.

1 Why do animals visit flowers? ▲
2 Why are insects attracted to sweet-smelling flowers? ▲
3 Why are the insects which pollinate carrion flowers unlikely to pollinate sweet-smelling flowers?
4 Would you expect bats to be more attracted by colour or scent? Explain.

5 *Red flowers in Britain are likely to be pollinated by moths and butterflies.* Explain why this is so.
6 **Try to find out** the names of some perfumes made from flowers.

DID YOU KNOW?

➲ Honeysuckle is pollinated by moths. It produces more scent in the evening than in the daytime.

➲ Bat-pollinated flowers produce huge amounts of pollen, enough to feed the bat and to pollinate the flowers.

In this heather burn in the Strath of Kildonan, Sutherland, a chemical reaction is taking place that converts the various chemicals in the heather and air into other, different chemicals. Burning is a dramatic chemical reaction, but there are other types, many of which are vitally important to us. The way that elements can be combined is the subject of this chapter, and the process of burning is looked at in more detail.

Look around you. How many different substances can you see in the room? Your list would likely contain wood, glass, paper, different plastics, metals, and many more. Add in the substances you can't see (the gases in the air) and the substances which make up your body (skin, hair, nails, blood...) and the list could go on and on. In fact there are over 1 000 000 different chemical substances in the world. That sounds very complicated.

But things are simpler than you might think. A heating experiment helps you to understand why. Bread, wood, plastic, and fingernail all seem to be very different from each other. When they are heated, however, they all leave the same black solid. That solid is called carbon. It is one of the simplest chemicals. It is an **element**. Bread, wood, plastic, and fingernail all contain the element carbon.

An element is a chemical substance which can't be broken down into anything simpler. That's because it is only made up of one type of atom. Carbon is called an element because it is only made up of carbon atoms.

There are over 100 different elements. Each has its own kind of atom. Around 90 elements have been found in nature. The rest have been made by scientists. You can see some of the natural elements in the photographs.

What's this black stuff, Holmes?

Elementary carbon, my dear Watson!

Sir Arthur Conan Doyle, creator of Sherlock Holmes, was born in Edinburgh in 1859. He studied medicine at the university there.

iodine

magnesium

sulphur

iron

bromine

carbon

zinc

mercury

silver

copper

1 What is an element? Why is carbon called an element? ▲
2 How many elements are there
   a in nature?
   b all together? ▲
3 From the elements in the photographs, pick out
   a *three* solids, *one* liquid, and *two* gases
   b elements used for making jewellery, water pipes, thermometers.

4 If you could see the 'atomic pictures' of iron, mercury, and oxygen, they would be different from each other. What would the differences be? Why are there differences?
5 Carbon is a black solid. How would you describe sulphur, oxygen?
6 **Try to find out** about uses of the element carbon.

You can find a list of all the elements on a chart called the periodic table of the elements. Each element is represented by a symbol – **H** stands for hydrogen, **He** for helium, **O** for oxygen, and so on.

Here is information about some common elements.

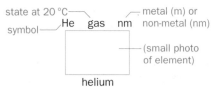

state at 20 °C ⎯ metal (m) or
He gas nm non-metal (nm)
symbol ⎯
(small photo of element)
helium

C solid nm   **Hg** _____ m   **O** gas _____   **S** _____ nm   **Fe** _____ nm

(colourless)

mercury   oxygen   sulphur

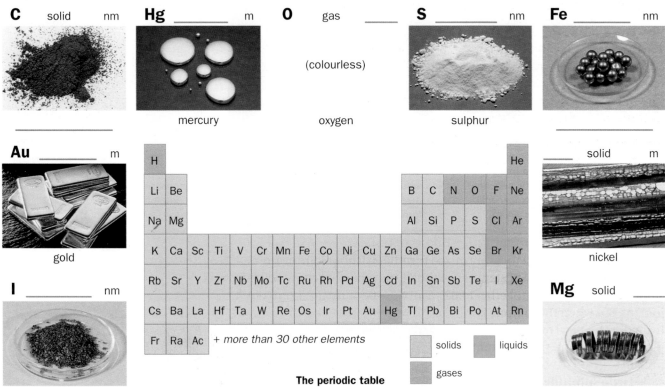

Au _____ m

gold

I _____ nm

iodine

The periodic table

solids   liquids

gases

solid m

nickel

Mg solid

These 100 elements make up all of the substances in the world. How can this be?

Most substances are made up of atoms of different elements joined together. The carbon dioxide in the air, for example, is made of carbon atoms joined to oxygen atoms. Carbon dioxide is a **compound – a chemical which has more than one type of atom in it.**

The elements carbon and oxygen

join up to give

the compound carbon dioxide.

1 What is the periodic table? ▲
2 Looking about the periodic table, what can you say about the numbers of
  a solids, liquids, and gases?
  b metals and non-metals? ▲
3 Which elements have the symbols O, C, Au, Hg, S?
4 What is a compound? Why is carbon dioxide called a compound?

5 Everything is made of only around 100 elements, but there are over 1 000 000 different chemicals. Explain this.
6 Look at the descriptions of the elements above.
  Then **try to find out**
  a the missing details
  b which elements are magnetic.

DID YOU KNOW?
➲ It can be helpful to think of the elements like the letters of the alphabet. Joining up different letters makes hundreds of thousands of words. Joining up atoms of different elements makes over a million different chemical compounds.

New compounds are made in chemical reactions. A chemical reaction between the elements iron and sulphur produces a new material: iron sulphide.

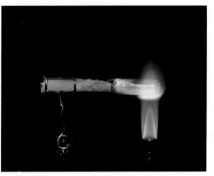

1 You can mix powdered iron and powdered sulphur without making a new chemical. You can still see the sulphur in the mixture. You can still pull the iron away with a magnet.

2 But if you heat a mixture of iron and sulphur (in a fume cupboard, for safety), a glow passes through the mixture. This time, a new chemical is formed.

3 The new chemical is the compound iron sulphide. It contains sulphur (but you can't see any yellow in it). It contains iron (but you cannot pull it away using a magnet).

Mixtures, chemical reactions, and compounds

When two or more substances are mixed together without joining up, a **mixture** is formed. The substances can usually be separated easily. Stirring sulphur and iron atoms together makes a mixture because the atoms don't join up. But when the mixture is heated, a chemical reaction takes place. The iron and sulphur atoms do join up to give a new **compound**. It is called **iron sulphide** because it is made of iron joined to sulphur.

Many everyday compounds are made when two elements join up. Salt is called **sodium chloride** because it is made by joining up sodium and chlorine atoms. Sand is **silicon oxide**. It has silicon and oxygen atoms joined up in it.

Common salt (sodium chloride)

Sand (silicon dioxide)

1 What happens in a chemical reaction? ▲

2 Why is it easier to separate atoms from a mixture than from a compound? ▲

3 Copper powder behaves like iron powder when it is mixed with sulphur. What would you expect to happen if the powders were

    a mixed?
    b heated together in a test tube?

4 Name the compounds made by joining up
    a copper and chlorine atoms
    b potassium and bromine atoms?

5 **Try to find out** the names of the main compounds found in
    a ruby   **b** rust
    c the 'rotten egg' gas.

DID YOU KNOW?

➲ Some compounds have five or more different elements joined together.

➲ The Space Shuttle uses hydrogen as a fuel. The clouds you see when it takes off are clouds of steam (hydrogen oxide).

Joining up makes a difference

Hydrogen is an element. It is a gas which burns well. It can even explode when you light it.

Oxygen is another element. It is a gas which helps things burn.

Hydrogen and oxygen join to give the compound **hydrogen oxide**. You know it better as water. It can put out some fires.

Compounds are usually different from the elements which make them up. And that's just as well! Your body is made up of a number of elements, some of which are very dangerous. These include chlorine (a poisonous gas), iodine (a poisonous solid), calcium, sodium, and potassium (which fizz in water), and phosphorous (which catches fire when it is dry). Fortunately, the elements are joined up in harmless compounds!

Joining up follows a pattern

In every chemical reaction, millions and millions of atoms are involved. But the atoms always follow a simple pattern when they join. When iron and sulphur join, for example, each iron atom joins with one sulphur atom. When hydrogen and oxygen join, two hydrogens join with one oxygen.

This means that we can give every compound a formula – a type of chemical shorthand which tells which atoms and how many atoms are joined up.

2 hydrogen atoms join with

1 oxygen atom to give

a water molecule (formula H_2O)

carbon dioxide
formula CO_2

hydrogen chloride
formula HCl

ammonia
formula NH_3

QUESTIONS

1 What is
 a the chemical name for water?
 b the formula for water? ▲
2 How is water different from the elements which make it up? ▲
3 Write down the name of a compound found in teeth. Then write down
 a which elements are in the compound
 b what each of the elements is like. ▲

4 a What is a formula? What does it tell you about a compound?
 b Name the compounds with the formula NaCl, MgO, CO, HCl. ▲
5 Milk is good for making teeth because it contains calcium. Is the calcium in milk the element form or in a compound? Explain.
6 **Try to find out** the difference between CO and CO_2.

DiD YOU KNOW?

➲ A compound can be more dangerous than the elements which make it up. Hydrogen sulphide – 'rotten egg' gas – is much more poisonous than hydrogen and sulphur.

➲ Much of your teeth is made of calcium phosphate, which contains calcium, phosphorus, and oxygen.

When a piece of very thin copper foil is put into chlorine gas, there is a flash of flame. A chemical reaction takes place. A blue-green solid called **copper chloride** is produced. Heat and light energy are produced, too. You can write down what happens in the reaction like this:

copper + chlorine ⟶ copper chloride + energy (heat and light)

This 'shorthand' way of writing down what happens is called a **chemical equation**.

The heat and light are produced when the copper and chlorine atoms join together. If you want to split up the copper chloride to get the copper and chlorine atoms back again, you have to supply energy. Electrical energy will do this:

copper chloride + electrical energy ⟶ copper + chlorine

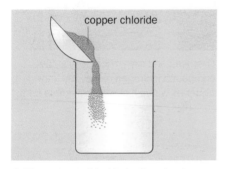

1 The copper chloride is dissolved.

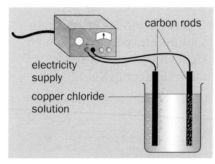

2 Carbon rods are put in the solution and connected up to an electrical supply.

3 As the current passes, solid copper and chlorine gas are produced.

In many reactions between elements, energy is produced. In these reactions, energy may have to be supplied to start the reaction off. But once it has started, a lot more energy is produced.

To split up compounds, energy is needed. The energy is needed to separate the joined atoms.

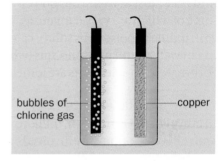

A huge amount of electricity is used to release aluminium from its compounds. Factories are often sited where electricity is cheap.

DID YOU KNOW?

➲ Aluminium, calcium, sodium, and magnesium are all produced from their compounds by using electricity.

➲ A reaction in which electricity is used to break up a compound is called an **electrolysis**.

---

1 How do you know that a chemical reaction takes place when thin copper foil is put in chlorine? (Give *two* pieces of evidence.) ▲

2 Why is energy needed to split up a compound? ▲

3 What is meant by an electrolysis? ▲

4 a Describe what you would do to produce copper and chlorine from copper chloride. ▲

b Is this reaction an electrolysis? Explain your answer.

5 Try to find out how silver plate is put on teaspoons.

Air is a mixture of more than ten different gases. The main gases are nitrogen, oxygen, carbon dioxide, and argon. The rest are present in tiny amounts.

Below, you can see information about the four main gases.

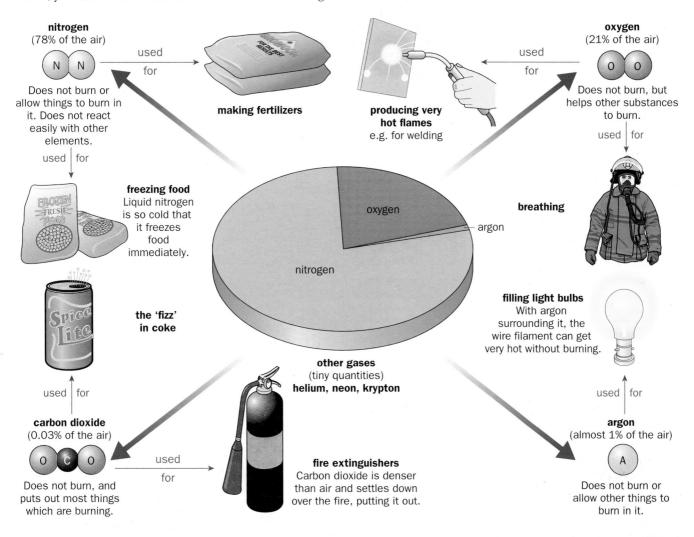

nitrogen
(78% of the air)

used for → **making fertilizers**

Does not burn or allow things to burn in it. Does not react easily with other elements.

used | for

freezing food
Liquid nitrogen is so cold that it freezes food immediately.

the 'fizz' in coke

used | for

carbon dioxide
(0.03% of the air)

Does not burn, and puts out most things which are burning.

used for →

fire extinguishers
Carbon dioxide is denser than air and settles down over the fire, putting it out.

producing very hot flames
e.g. for welding

oxygen
(21% of the air)

used for

Does not burn, but helps other substances to burn.

used | for

breathing

filling light bulbs
With argon surrounding it, the wire filament can get very hot without burning.

used | for

argon
(almost 1% of the air)

Does not burn or allow other things to burn in it.

other gases
(tiny quantities)
helium, neon, krypton

oxygen

argon

nitrogen

---

1 **a** Put the main four gases in air in order, with the most plentiful first.
  b How much of each gas is there in 100 cm^3 of air?
2 Which gases are
  a elements? **b** molecules? Explain your answers. In which way is argon 'the odd one out'?
3 **a** Which gases put out things which are burning?
  b Which gas helps things to burn?

4 Why is
  a carbon dioxide a good gas for fire extinguishers?
  b liquid nitrogen used to freeze food?
  c argon used in light bulbs?
5 Why are cylinders of oxygen used in hospitals and by welders?
6 **Try to find out**
  a what the other gases in the air are used for
  b what dry ice is and why it is useful.

DID YOU KNOW?
➲ The atmospheres on Venus and Mars are made up almost completely of carbon dioxide.
➲ Earth's atmosphere contains water vapour. That's where the rain comes from.

Carbon dioxide

Carbon dioxide can be made in the science lab by adding hydrochloric acid to marble chips (calcium carbonate).

If you want to test a gas to see if it is carbon dioxide, you should bubble it through lime water. **Carbon dioxide turns lime water milky.**

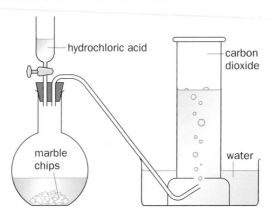

The lime water test

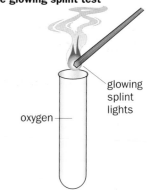

limewater goes cloudy

Oxygen

Oxygen can be made by dropping hydrogen peroxide on to potassium permanganate.

To find out if a gas is oxygen, you should light a splint, blow it out then put the glowing splint in the gas. **Oxygen will make the glowing splint light up again.**

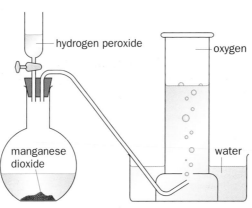

The glowing splint test

glowing splint lights

oxygen

Hydrogen

Hydrogen can be made by adding hydrochloric acid to zinc.

The test for hydrogen gas is to light it. **Hydrogen burns with a 'pop' when it is mixed with air.**

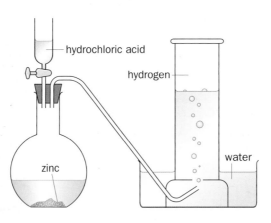

The hydrogen test

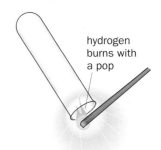

hydrogen burns with a pop

---

1 What do you need to make
   a carbon dioxide?
   b hydrogen?
2 How can you test a gas to see if it is oxygen?
3 The gas given off when you open a bottle of lemonade turns lime water milky. What does this tell you about it?
4 Look at how each gas is collected. The method depends on whether the gas is more or less dense than air. What can you say about the densities of the three gases?
5 **Try to find out** how oxygen is produced for industrial use.

DiD YOU KNOW?
➲ Nitrogen does nothing in each of these tests.
➲ Much of the carbon dioxide used by industry is produced when whisky is made.

You see things burn every day, but how closely do you observe what happens? Have you noticed that...

...when things are burned, they are permanently changed

This means that burning is different from just heating. When you heat food in a plastic container in a microwave, the container gets hot. But when it cools down again, it is unchanged. If you set fire to a piece of plastic, however, it burns with a black sooty flame. It is totally changed. **(Don't do this, however, because burning plastic can give off very poisonous fumes.)**

This means that burning must be a chemical reaction. The chemicals in the material which is burned are changed into new chemicals.

...some things burn well, but some things don't

Stone, brick, iron, and steel don't normally burn. That's why they are used to make fire places and fuel-burning stoves. But many other substances do burn well. Wood, coal, paper, oil, petrol, paraffin, natural gas, and plastics all burn well. Some of them burn so well that we use them to heat our homes.

Substances which can burn are said to be **flammable**.

...when substances burn, things usually happen in the same way

1 First, the substance has to be lit.
2 Once it is lit, the substance burns on its own – as long as it has enough air. If there is a very good flow of air, it burns with a blue flame. If not, it burns with a yellow smoky flame.
3 At the end, the substance seems to have disappeared. Usually all that is left is some ash and black cinders.

...it's possible to change the rate of burning

⊃ If you improve the air supply, burning is faster. Cutting down the air supply (e.g. by putting a fire blanket over the fire) makes burning slow down – or even stop.
⊃ Cooling down a fire (e.g. by pouring water on it) can also make it slow down or stop.

1 Write down *three* things you notice when a match burns.
2 What are flammable substances? Name some. ▲
3 What is needed to keep something burning? ▲
4 What can slow down burning? Why does this work? ▲
5 Give evidence that burning is a chemical reaction.
6 **Try to find out**
  a what the fire triangle tells you
  b how to put out different types of fire.

DiD YOU KNOW?
⊃ Iron and aluminium can burn at very high temperatures. Powdered aluminium and iron burn to make the sparks in 'sparkler' fireworks

Look what happens in these three experiments on burning.

Experiment 1 When the test tube is put over the burning candle, the candle goes out and the water level rises inside the test tube.

This suggests that the candle needs one of the gases of the air to burn. It goes out when this gas is used up.

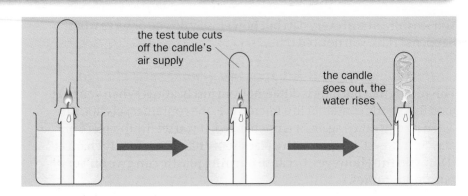

the test tube cuts off the candle's air supply

the candle goes out, the water rises

Experiment 2 Magnesium ribbon burns with a brilliant white flame. A white ash is formed.

If you weigh the ribbon before burning, and weigh the ash at the end, you find that the ash is heavier than the ribbon was. **This means that the burning ribbon must have joined up with something – most likely a gas from the air.**

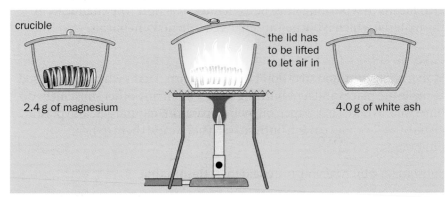

crucible

2.4 g of magnesium

the lid has to be lifted to let air in

4.0 g of white ash

Experiment 3 When carbon is burned in air, the gas produced turns lime water milky. This shows that **when carbon burns, it joins up with oxygen.**

When anything burns, it joins up with oxygen. When an element burns, a new compound, called the oxide, is made.

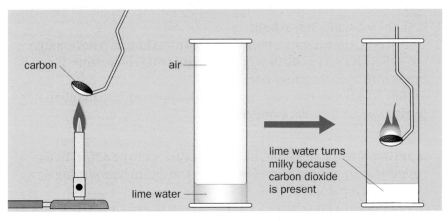

carbon

air

lime water

lime water turns milky because carbon dioxide is present

The water level rose in the test tube (experiment 1) because the burning candle used up the oxygen in the air.

The ash produced (experiment 2) was magnesium oxide. It contained the magnesium in the ribbon joined with oxygen from the air. That's why it was heavier than the ribbon had been.

1 a What happens when an element burns?
b What is the name of the chemical produced?
2 What gas is made when carbon burns in air? How can you show this?
3 Why does
a the candle go out in experiment 1?
b the ash weigh more than the magnesium ribbon in experiment 2?
4 When petrol burns, carbon dioxide and water (hydrogen oxide) are produced. What elements make up petrol?

DID YOU KNOW?
➲ Magnesium burns with such a bright light that it is used in lifeboat emergency flares. The flare is fired high into the air and floats there supported by a parachute.

Burning is a really useful reaction

The energy from burning fuels is vital for our way of life. Burning fuels heat our homes, drive cars, ships, and aeroplanes, and are used by most of the power stations which generate our electricity.

Most of the fuels we use, like natural gas, petrol, and diesel, are **hydrocarbons**. These are chemical compounds which are made up of carbon and hydrogen atoms. When they burn with good supplies of air, the chemicals they produce are safe. The carbon atoms join up with the oxygen to make carbon dioxide, which is harmless in small amounts. The hydrogen atoms join up with the oxygen to make water, which is perfectly safe! If the air supply is poor, however, the fuel won't burn completely. Carbon monoxide, a very poisonous gas, is made. It's very dangerous because it has no smell.

Power stations burn millions of tons of fuel.

Burning can be very dangerous

It has to be used with great care in the home.

One of the dangers comes from carbon monoxide. Faulty fires and boilers which don't have good supplies of air will give off this gas.

All **flammable materials** (materials which burn) have to be kept away from fire. Some materials used for making clothes (nylon, polyester) melt and give really nasty burns when they are on fire. The foam in some furniture gives off highly poisonous gases even when smouldering.

possible danger
gas fire

Be safe!
1 **Check the flame colour** (orange flames mean danger).
2 **Check the chimney or flue** (it must not be blocked).
3 **Check the air supply in the room** (vents must not be covered).
4 **Have the fire checked every year.**

possible danger
flammable material

Be safe!
1 **Check the labels on furniture** (make sure the fabric is fire-resistant).
2 **If you are wearing long clothes, stay away from fires.**
3 **Don't use matches or candles near flammable materials** (and don't let adults put cigarettes on them either!).

1 a What is heat energy used to do in your home?
  b Do you burn any fuels at home? If so, what?
2 What is a hydrocarbon? ▲
3 Why is it dangerous when fuels don't have enough air to burn?

4 Write down *three* safety rules for using a gas fire in the home.
5 20-year-old furniture could be a fire hazard. Why?
6 **Try to find out** all you can about smoke detectors.

DiD YOU KNOW?
➲ Banning very flammable furniture materials (in 1988) saved over 700 lives in the first ten years.
➲ All the clothing worn by motor racing drivers – even their underwear – is made of fire-proof fabric.

Air pollution...

We depend on burning fuels but we have to use them carefully. Burning fuels causes air pollution by putting harmful substances into the air. Here are some of these substances.

Air pollutant	How it is produced	Harmful effects
carbon monoxide	by burning fuels without enough air for complete burning – cars produces lots of it	poisonous – a particular problem where there are lots of cars
carbon (sooty smoke)	by burning fuels (especially coal) without enough air for complete burning	Makes everything very dirty, causes asthma
carbon dioxide	even an efficient fuel burner makes this	is causing the atmosphere to overheat – **global warming**
sulphur dioxide	by burning fuels which contain sulphur compounds (most do)	dissolves to make **'acid rain'**, which eats away stone and metal and poisons plants and humans

Sulphur dioxide is released into the air at petrol refineries.

...and how to reduce it

There are steps which can be taken to cut down air pollution:

⊃ Councils have cut down the amount of soot in the air by making 'smokeless zones' where no homes can burn smoky fuels.

⊃ The amount of carbon monoxide can be cut down by servicing cars, boilers, and gas fires regularly to make the burning efficient.

⊃ Petrol companies can remove the sulphur from the fuel they produce.

⊃ Power stations which burn fuel can pass the fumes through water. Sulphur dioxide dissolves very well, and this removes it.

There is one thing which we can all do to help. **We can all make sure that less fuel is burned by using less energy** – use less electricity, buy small cars, use trains, buses, or bicycles to travel.

This really is important. Even when fuels are burned efficiently, carbon dioxide is produced. And carbon dioxide is the main gas which causes global warming.

These trees were killed by small amounts of sulphur dioxide in the air.

1 What is
a air pollution?
b a smokeless zone? ▲
2 Choose *two* air pollutants. Write down
a how they are formed
b how the amounts of each in the atmosphere can be reduced. ▲

3 a How can we cut down on the energy we use?
b Why does travelling by bus cut down on energy use?
4 Why does switching off lights save on fuel?
5 **Try to find out** which countries burn the most fuels.

DID YOU KNOW?

⊃ The smaller the amount of pollution produced by a car, the cheaper the car licence is.

⊃ To cover a kilometre, a car driver requires 6 times more energy than a train passenger and 50 times more energy than a cyclist.

The Sun heats up the Earth

This is what happens to the heat:

1 Heat radiation from the Sun passes through the atmosphere and strikes the Earth's surface.
2 Most of the heat is taken in by the Earth and warms it.
3 Some of the heat is reflected back. Most of this heat escapes into space.

But it's not all good news:

4 Some of the reflected heat, however, is trapped by 'greenhouse gases' in the atmosphere. And that causes **global warming**.

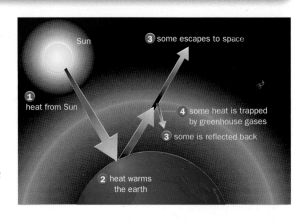

① heat from Sun
② heat warms the earth
③ some escapes to space
④ some heat is trapped by greenhouse gases
③ some is reflected back

Global warming…

There is no doubt that the Earth is slowly heating up. The main reason for this is that we are producing more and more of one main greenhouse gas – carbon dioxide. More carbon dioxide in the atmosphere means that less heat can escape.

…and the effects it causes

In the last 100 years, the temperature of the Earth's surface has risen by 0.5 °C. That may not seem too much, but temperature rises like this will make a difference:

➲ Sea levels will rise.

➲ More ice in the Arctic and Antarctic will melt.

➲ Weather patterns will change. British weather will become windier and wetter, with more floods.

➲ In some parts of the world, there will be more droughts. Deserts will get bigger.

➲ Crops which once could grow successfully in some areas will grow more poorly, if at all.

➲ Mosquitoes and other insects which live in warm areas will spread to new areas, carrying disease.

It's really important to cut down on the gases!!!

Global temperature changes (1880–2000)

departure from long-term mean (°C) vs *year*

Malaria-carrying mosquitoes will arrive in northern climes if global warming continues.

---

1 What happens to the heat which reaches Earth from the Sun? ▲

2 What is global warming? What causes it? ▲

3 What information can you get from the temperature graph?

4 Write down some effects of global warming. ▲

5 What problems do you think will be caused by
   a deserts getting bigger?
   b mosquitoes moving into new areas?

6 **Try to find out** what ozone is, how it is produced, and why it is important.

DiD YOU KNOW?

➲ The greenhouse gases are so named because they do the same job as the glass in a greenhouse: keep heat in.

➲ We need *some* greenhouse gases in the atmosphere – without them the average temperature on the Earth would be about 33 °C lower, and it is unlikely that life as we know it would be able to exist.

An ideal fuel should burn:

⊃ giving lots of energy

⊃ safely

⊃ giving no pollution.

In fact, hydrogen does all of these things.

⊃ It gives three times as much energy as petrol.

⊃ Because it is less dense than air, it quickly floats upwards, away from any leaks.

⊃ When it burns, it only produces water.

On this evidence, hydrogen should be the most widely used fuel of all.

The Space Shuttle and how it works

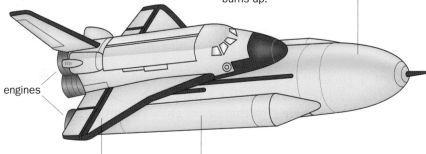

The fuel tank carries fuel for the Orbiter's engine. The fuel is used up just as the Orbiter enters orbit at a height of 200 km. Then the tank is ejected. It enters the atmosphere and burns up.

engines

The Orbiter is designed to go into orbit, carry out its mission, and return to Earth. It carries a little fuel.

Booster rockets help the Shuttle to get off the ground. When the Shuttle has reached a height of 500 km, the fuel in these rockets is completely used up. The rockets are ejected. They parachute back to Earth to be used again.

Hydrogen **is** used as a fuel. It is used for welding metals and it is used as a fuel for space rockets. (It is the main fuel for the Space Shuttle.) But there are snags which prevent it from being used more.

⊃ **A good fuel should be cheap and easy to produce**, but hydrogen can't be made cheaply yet. Hydrogen comes from water, and there is plenty of that! But the methods used, such as passing an electric current through water, are not cheap.

⊃ **A good fuel should be easily stored**, and that's another problem. Hydrogen can be stored in strong tanks and moved through pipes. That makes it useful in industry and in homes. But the storage tanks are really too heavy to carry in cars.

There is hope, however. Scientists have discovered a way to get hydrogen from water using sunlight. If it can be made to work on a large scale, it will produce hydrogen cheaply. And they are working hard to find other ways of storing the hydrogen. If they can solve these problems, hydrogen will be the fuel of the future.

Hydrogen-powered vehicles – tomorrow's transport?

1 Why is hydrogen a good fuel? ▲

2 Why does the Space Shuttle carry
   a hydrogen?
   b oxygen?

3 Why are clouds of steam produced when the Shuttle takes off?

4 Why is hydrogen not used more widely as a fuel? What problems are scientists trying to overcome to allow us to use it?

5 Using hydrogen instead of other fuels will cut down pollution. Why?

6 Write down what happens to each part of the Shuttle. Then draw a diagram to describe what happens as it goes into orbit.

DID YOU KNOW?

⊃ A hydrogen–oxygen flame is hot enough to weld under water.

⊃ The Space Shuttle carries 600 tonnes of fuel. When it is taking off, it burns 4 tonnes of fuel every second.

We are able to survive on this planet within a fairly narrow range of temperatures, relative to the cold of outer space or the intense heat of the inside of a star like the Sun. Our ability to control the flow of heat is important in smaller practical ways, too. Modern insulating materials have made it possible for people to survive for long periods in icy highland mountain conditions such as those in the Cairngorms. In an emergency, this extra protection can often mean the difference between life and death. In this chapter, you will be introduced to temperature and heat and how heat can be transferred.

Although some coal is available on the surface of the Earth, most has to be mined from deep underground.

Many North Sea oil rigs have direct pipelines to Sullom Voe in the Shetland Isles.

At one time peat was commonly used as a fuel. It is more scarce now.

Petrol and diesel are made from crude oil.

All these things burn – they all release energy to be used elsewhere.

They all make things happen.

Alcohol can be used to power cars, too…

…and so can liquified hydrogen gas.

Paraffin was first refined for heating and lighting near Edinburgh by a Scot, James Young (1811–1883).

And all of these burn, too…

1 Name the various fuels in the pictures above. ▲
2 **Try to find out** where the alcohol for cars is used and what it is made from.

The amount of energy which your body needs each day depends on a number of different things. It depends on your age, your size, whether you are a boy or a girl, how active you are, and other things, too. It's impossible to calculate exactly how much 'energy food' you should eat in a day, but that does not matter. As long as you eat roughly the correct amount, you should have no energy problems.

The people who do have energy problems are those who eat far too much or far too little energy food. Jonathan and Rajan have energy problems. But their problems are very different!

The lists on the right show the food which Jonathan and Rajan could eat in a normal day. The energy contains in the food is given too.
It is measured in **kilojoules (kJ)**:

Jonathan's food	Amount	Energy supplied
porridge (1 bowl)	100 g	500 kJ
bacon (2 rashers)	75 g	1430 kJ
eggs (2)	100 g	660 kJ
meat pie	100 g	1200 kJ
potatoes (4)	250 g	1600 kJ
apple pie	100 g	2000 kJ
custard	60 g	280 kJ
sausages (4)	250 g	2300 kJ
chips	110 g	900 kJ
beans	125 g	460 kJ
bread (6 slices)	100 g	2000 kJ
butter (on bread)	30 g	1000 kJ
cake (2 slices)	100 g	1350 kJ
sugar (in tea)	40 g	800 kJ
biscuits (3)	60 g	1200 kJ
chocolate (1 bar)	100 g	2500 kJ

Jonathan

- lives in Scotland
- works in an office
- drives to work
- reads, and watches television in his spare time.

DiD YOU KNOW?

- You will often hear people refer to food energy in **calories**, e.g. *counting calories.*
- 4.2 kJ = 1 calorie
- Scotland has one of the highest rates of heart disease in the world and the highest in the European Union.

Rajan

- lives in South India
- works on his small 'farm'
- works all day, and has little spare time.

Rajan's food	Amount	Energy supplied
rice (2 bowls)	400 g	2350 kJ
potato (1)	125 g	400 kJ
beans (1 bowl)	180 g	1650 kJ
other vegetables	350 g	450 kJ
banana (2)	200 g	600 kJ
sugar (2 spoons)	25 g	470 kJ
milk	125 g	370 kJ
coconut oil	25 g	900 kJ

1 What unit is used to measure food energy? ▲
2 Different people should eat different amounts of energy food. Explain why. ▲
3 Men normally need between 11 000 and 15 000 kJ of energy in a day. Office workers need around 11 000 kJ. Labourers need around 15 000 kJ. Explain the difference.
4 Add the number of kJ in
   a Jonathan's food
   b Rajan's food.
5 Energy food which is not used up is changed to fat.
   a Explain why Jonathan is so overweight.
   b Which foods should he cut out if he wants to slim?
c What else could he do to lose weight?
6 Rajan is often too tired to work hard. Explain why.
7 **Try to find out** why so many people in the world are short of food and what can be done about it.

103

Coal (and peat)

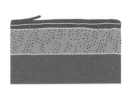

2 The action of bacteria changed the decaying plants to peat. Peat is used as a fuel in some countries. It is the first stage in the formation of coal.

3 Gradually the land sank and water covered it. Layers of mud and gravel were laid over the decaying plants. As more and more rocks were laid down by the seas above, the pressure on the peat layers increased. The temperature also got higher.

1 Coal was formed from the remains of plants which grew in huge forests about 300 million years ago! As the plants died, they fell down and began to rot. The decaying plants formed a thick layer on the wet and swampy floor of the forest.

Stages in the formation of coal.

4 Eventually, over millions of years, the decaying plants were changed into coal.

Now much of this coal lies deep underground, covered by large amounts of sediment. To mine these underground coal seams, deep shafts have to be sunk.

Oil (and gas)

When areas such as the North Sea were warmer and shallower than they are now, countless millions of tiny animals and plants lived there. When these organisms died, their bodies fell to the sea bed. There they were trapped in sand and mud, which formed as sediment.

Pressure changed the sand and mud to sandstone and mudstone. Pressure, and heat, changed the organisms to oil and gas.

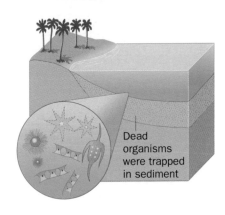

Dead organisms were trapped in sediment

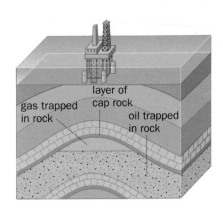

layer of cap rock

gas trapped in rock

oil trapped in rock

The underground pressure forces some oil (and gas) upwards, through the rock. But most oil and gas has to be drilled for.

---

1 a What were coal, peat, and oil formed from? ▲
b How were these fuels formed?
2 Why is coal a fossil fuel? Name another fossil fuel. ▲
3 Oil is not found in underground pools. How is it found? ▲
4 Sometimes, oil can rise to the surface without pumping. Suggest why this happens.

5 The energy stored in coal came from the Sun. Explain this.
6 Try to find out
a about the oil industry in Scotland
b which other countries have large oilfields
c which countries have large coalfields.

DİD YOU KNOW?
➲ Coal is called a **fossil fuel** because it was made from things which lived on the Earth long ago.
➲ The oil which comes out of the Earth is hot. It can be as hot as 80 °C.

Hotness or coldness

When you touch something, your senses tell you immediately whether it feels hot or cold. Too hot, and you'll move your fingers very quickly! The idea that you've touched something hot does give you the idea that there's a lot of energy in whatever you've touched.

Accidentally touch a single spark from a firework and it's very hot, but there's not much heat energy in it. Drink a cup of tea and the temperature is not high, but the heat energy can burn your tongue!

Heat and temperature are different

Certainly it's true that something that increases its energy increases its temperature (so is the reverse).

Heat is a measure of energy. It is measured in joules (J) (or kilojoules (kJ)).

Temperature is a measure of hotness (or coldness) and is measured in degrees Celsius (°C). Temperature is measured with a **thermometer**.

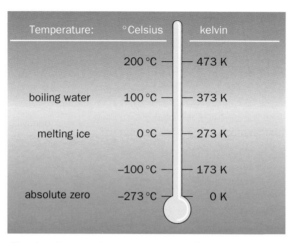

Absolute temperatures are measured on a scale starting at minus 273 °C. This temperature scale is named after Lord Kelvin, who first produced it. A change in temperature of one kelvin (1 K) is the same as a change of 1 °C.

The physicist William Thomson, Lord Kelvin of Largs (1824–1907)

Stopping the vibrations

You've seen that solids, liquids, and gases are made up of tiny particles. In solids, these particles vibrate, and the larger their vibrations, the more energy they have. The opposite is also true: as they lose energy, the size of their vibrations gets smaller. This change in energy is what heat is.

If you keep on cooling the solid, you are removing heat energy, and the particles' vibrations should keep on getting smaller until they stop vibrating completely. Now, you can't have a vibration which is smaller than nothing. So, theory predicts a point at which vibrations cease. **Absolute zero** is the name given to the temperature at which this happens – the point at which a material has no heat energy. This temperature is –273 °C.

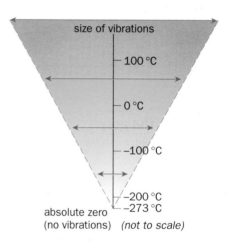

1 Heat energy is a descriptions for _____ particles. ▲
2 Temperature is a description for _____ or _____. ▲
3 Heat is measured in _____ (or _____). ▲
4 Temperature is measured in _____. ▲
5 Which has most heat energy: a cup of water at 60°C or a firework spark at 1000°C?

Experiment 1

The mug shown below was filled with hot water at 45 °C. The temperature of the water was taken at regular intervals during the school day.

Common sense will tell you that the temperature will go down, as heat energy is returned to the surroundings.

digital thermometer

water

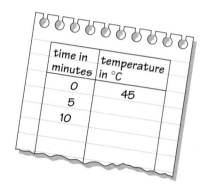

time in minutes	temperature in °C
0	45
5	
10	

The mug of water has cooled during the school day from 45 °C to 25 °C. It will continue losing heat energy and the temperature will continue to drop until the temperature reaches the environmental temperature.

The temperature will continue to drop until it reaches room temperature.

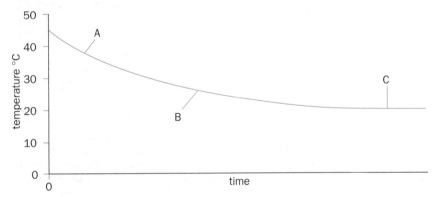

The graph shows how the temperature steadily reduces.

Reading the graph

The graph below shows how most substances cool after being taken away from the source of heat.

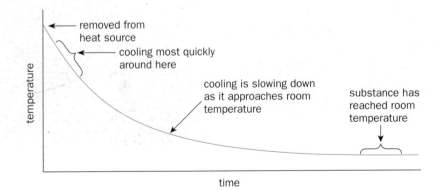

removed from heat source

cooling most quickly around here

cooling is slowing down as it approaches room temperature

substance has reached room temperature

QUESTIONS

1 In the top graph
  a where is the heat loss the greatest: A, B, or C? ▲
  b What is the temperature at point B? ▲
2 What is the room temperature?
3 Draw a simple cooling graph like the bottom graph. Add two more cooling graph lines with the following characteristics:
  a same starting temperature, higher room temperature
  b higher starting temperature, lower room temperature.
4 How would you double the amount of heat in experiment 1? What do you think would be the effect on the graph?
5 Plan an experiment similar to the ones above using different locations measured over a 24-hour period.

All materials are made from particles

You have seen that every material thing is made of particles – atoms and molecules – that are constantly on the move. As a material gains heat energy, the particles will move faster. If heat energy is removed, the particles will move slower. This idea is known as the **kinetic theory**.

Solid

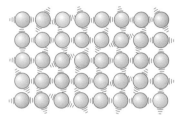

Least heat energy: each particle vibrates around its fixed place in the framework. Example: ice.

Liquid

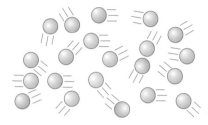

More heat energy: particles are free to move faster and change positions. Example: water.

Gas

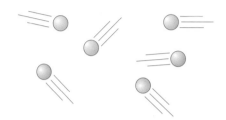

Most heat energy: particles move faster still and are free to move in any direction. Example: steam.

The kinetic theory can explain the following behaviour of materials:

⮑ **Melting** If some solids are warmed, the particle vibrations increase until the particles start to break free and become part of a liquid.

⮑ **Evaporation** If heat energy is supplied to the liquid, the particles in the liquid move faster. At the surface, the faster particles may break free of the liquid and form a gas above it.

⮑ **Condensing** When heat energy is removed from a gas, its temperature falls. The particles in the gas move closer together. At a certain stage, they will come close enough to form a liquid.

⮑ **Freezing** As a liquid cools down, the vibrations of the particles get smaller. At a certain temperature they start to move into the 'framework' formation which is typical of a solid.

⮑ **Mass is conserved** In these changes of state, only the behaviour of the particles changes. The actual particles are the same throughout. Because of this, the total mass of substance remains the same.

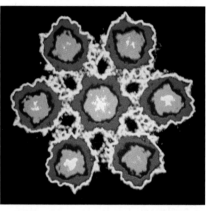

Uranium atoms arranged in a perfect hexagonal shape around a central atom in a crystal. Although they are locked in this framework, they are always vibrating.

QUESTIONS

1 Describe what happens to the particles of a liquid as it is heated. ▲

2 What is the name for the change from gas to liquid. Give an example of where you have seen this happening. ▲

3 Where does the heat energy come from to melt an ice cube which is left on a kitchen work surface?

4 **Try to find out** how the kinetic theory explains
 a diffusion (for example, the spread of a smell)
 b how a solid dissolves in a liquid.

DID YOU KNOW?

⮑ Different substances change state at different temperatures for a given pressure. Water freezes at 0 °C and boils at 100 °C. Mercury freezes at −39 °C and boils at 357 °C. Some thermometers use alcohol, which freezes at −117 °C and boils at 78 °C.

Conductors and insulators...

Heat can travel through solids. If you have ever tried to stir boiling soup using a metal spoon, you will know that. Heat energy quickly flows from the soup, through the spoon, to your hand. Your fingers begin to get hot!

The movement of heat through the solid metal is called **conduction**. The metal spoon **conducts** heat from the hot soup to your hand. The metal is called a good conductor because heat can flow easily through it. If you touch something like ice or a metal, the reverse happens. Heat flows **from** your finger (ice warms and melts).

If you do have to stir hot soup, it's much more sensible to use a wooden spoon or a spoon with a plastic handle. Like most other non-metals, wood and plastic don't allow heat to flow easily through them. Substances like these are called insulators. They even feel 'warm' to the touch.

You can stir boiling soup with a metal spoon, but not for long!

...and their uses

Conductors and insulators can both be useful, but for different jobs. The bottom of a saucepan may be made from a metal, like iron or aluminium, which lets heat flow quickly from the cooker to the food inside. But its handle is likely to be wooden or plastic. These materials won't let heat flow to your fingers and burn them.

Conduction and the kinetic theory

The bar starts off cold. When a burner is placed under the left-hand end, the particles there gain energy. They vibrate more.

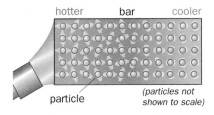

hotter   bar   cooler

particle   *(particles not shown to scale)*

The particles next to them on the right are made to vibrate more than they were, but a little bit less than those on their left. In turn, the particles on their right are made to vibrate more than they were, but a little bit less than those on their left. Soon, even the molecules at the right of the bar are vibrating more than they were, and the end of the bar on the right is now hotter than it was originally. Heat has been conducted along the bar.

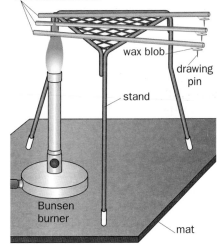

different materials

wax blob

drawing pin

stand

Bunsen burner

mat

You can investigate conduction using simple apparatus like this.

1 What is meant by saying that
  a the metal spoon conducts heat?
  b wood is an insulator? ▲

2 **a** Which substances are conductors and which are insulators? ▲
  b Pick out the conductors and insulators from this list:
  aluminium wool glass tin iron cork plastic air

3 Why is **a** the base of a saucepan made of metal?
  b the handle made of plastic? ▲

4 How could you protect yourself if you had to lift a hot plate? Why would this protect you?

5 Explain the idea of conduction using the words 'vibrations' and 'particles'.

6 How would you investigate conduction using the apparatus on the right above?

DiD YOU KNOW?

➲ Copper and silver are the best heat conductors. Copper conducts heat ten times better than iron. Gases are the poorest conductors. In other words, they are the best insulators.

➲ When heat travels by conduction, the energy is passed on from one atom to the next. The heat flows, the 'heated' atoms don't!

On the move through fluids

Heat energy can travel through liquids. This must happen when you boil water in an electric kettle. The kettle's heating element only warms the water next to it, but the heat energy is carried all through the water until it boils.

Heat energy can travel through gases. This must happen when you heat a room using an electric convector heater. The heater only warms the air inside it, but soon you can feel the warmth all through the room. Cooler, more-dense air moves into the bottom of the heater; warmer, less-dense air is pushed out at the top. Smoke rises by convection. When the air above a fire is heated, it rises, carrying tiny particles of ash with it. The heat can't be travelling through the water or air by *conduction*. (Water and air are both bad conductors.) The heat travels in a different way, by **convection**.

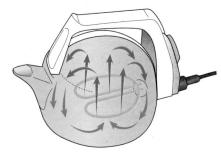

→ heated water moves in this direction
→ cold water moves in this direction

How heat energy travels through the water in the kettle.

Termites are convection experts

Although termites are only small animals, they have found a way to keep cooler in hotter climates. They use convection to best advantage in their termite mounds.

Two experiments

The diagrams below show how you can demonstrate convection currents very easily.

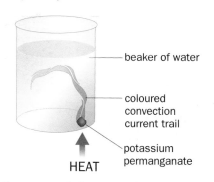

— beaker of water
— coloured convection current trail
— potassium permanganate
HEAT

You can watch the convection current trail of potassium permanganate.

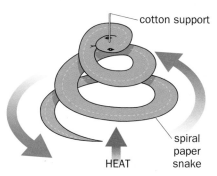

cotton support
spiral paper snake
HEAT

The spiral paper snake will rotate when held over a heat source. The rising convection current makes the snake turn.

A termite mound is like a big chimney. or set of chimneys. Inside are chambers and funnels that allow convection currents to circulate. Cooler, more-dense air moves in at the bottom, and warmer, less-dense air is expelled at the top. Termites are 'cool' animals!

Density drives convection

Convection currents move because the cooler, denser fluid moves in at the 'bottom', forcing warmer, less-dense fluid to rise. (So, convection *cannot* take place in solids!)

1 Copy and complete:
  a Heat travels through _____ and _____ by convection.
  b Convection takes place whenever...
  c Heat can't travel through solids by convection because... ▲

2 a Explain how a convector heater warms all the air in a room. ▲
  b If you fix paper decorations to a wall above a convector heater, they flutter when the heater is switched on. Why does this happen?

3 Why is it difficult to heat rooms with high ceilings?

4 On which shelf of an oven do cakes cook quickest, and why?

5 The wall above a radiator is often dirty with dust from the floor. How does the dust get there?

6 **Try to find out** why firemen enter smoke-filled rooms by crawling.

When you toast bread under the grill, some heat travels **downwards**, from the grill's heating element to the toast.

This heat can't be carried by *convection*. Convection carries hot air upwards.

The heat can't have been *conducted* to the bread either. The air between the bread and the grill is a poor conductor.

The heat is travelling by **radiation**.

grill element

toast

The two-can experiment

Infrared radiation is much more efficient from dull surfaces. Dull, dark surfaces are better absorbers and emitters of radiation. Bright, shiny surfaces are better reflectors of radiation.

The two-can experiment shown below demonstrates this. The graph shows that the dark can cools more rapidly.

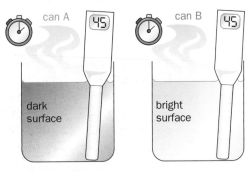

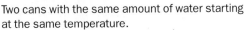

can A 45   can B 45

45

temperature

can B

can A

time

Two cans with the same amount of water starting at the same temperature.

Can A cools more quickly than can B.

Earth-warming radiation

The Earth is warmed by heat radiation. This comes from the Sun. (The Sun also gives off other kinds of radiation, including light.) Only a small fraction of the Sun's heat radiation reaches the Earth. **Heat radiation is not carried by moving material particles**, since space has very few of them .

When the heat radiation reaches the Earth, some of it is taken in, or **absorbed**. Some is bounced back, or **reflected**. It's the absorbed heat which warms up the Earth. **The more heat that is absorbed, the hotter it gets**.

Clouds can cut down the amount of heat radiation reaching the Earth. Cloudy days are usually cool days! That's because **heat radiation travels in straight lines**. The heat can't bend round the edges of the cloud to reach the Earth underneath.

The (infrared) heat radiation emitted from the Sun takes about 8 minutes to reach the Earth.

1 Explain why heat radiation can't be travelling from the grill to the toast by conduction or convection. ▲
2 What is meant by
   a absorbing heat? ▲
   b reflecting heat? ▲
3 What happens to an object when it absorbs heat?
4 Why can heat travel through space by radiation, but not by conduction or convection?
5 Give evidence which shows that radiated heat travels in straight lines.
6 a What is infrared radiation? ▲
   b **Try to find out** some uses of infrared detectors.

A load of hot air

It's hard to believe, but it's true. The man in the photograph is kept warm by the holes in his string vest! The air in the holes is what matters. When the man pulls on his shirt, it traps air in the holes in the vest. Air is an excellent insulator. It prevents his body heat from escaping and so keeps him warm.

A string vest may seem to be a rather strange piece of clothing, but, in fact, all of your clothes keep you warm in the same way. Clothes have tiny pockets of air trapped between their fibres and so act as insulators. This insulation is important because everyone has the problem of heat loss. Your body is warmer than the air around you and so it is always losing heat. The insulation supplied by clothes cuts down the amount of heat which escapes and so saves valuable energy.

For a long time, the warmest clothes were made out of natural materials like wool, fur, and feathers. These all have tiny pockets of air trapped in them and are excellent insulators. But now manufactured fibres are often used instead. A warm anorak is likely to be filled with thousands of fibres made of a plastic such as polyester – with air trapped between them.

Here are some other manufactured insulators.

The holes in his string vest actually help to keep the man warm.

This flask can keep drinks warm for 5 hours. It contains an insulating layer of hard plastic foam with air bubbles trapped in it (expanded polystyrene). Some flasks contain a twin-walled glass container – rather like a tube of double-glazing. These are called Thermos or Dewar flasks (after the Scottish scientist James Dewar, 1842–1923).

Mountaineers' clothing is filled with a layer of manufactured fibres. The warmest clothing is filled with a special hollow fibre. It actually has air trapped inside it.

This swimming pool cover is made of plastic sheeting with bubbles of air trapped in it. The air helps the cover to float. It also stops the water from cooling down by loss of heat.

DiD YOU KNOW?

- All mammals and birds lose heat. But, apart from humans, all have enough 'natural insulation' to allow them to survive.
- Snow is a good insulator. It has air trapped in it.

QUESTIONS

1 Why is a string vest a good insulator? ▲
2 What is the 'problem of heat loss' which affects you (and other mammals and birds)? How do you overcome this problem? ▲
3 Make a list of all the air-filled insulators mentioned on this page. ▲
4 What kinds of 'natural insulation' do birds and mammals have?
5 What makes an air-filled swimming pool cover useful? ▲
6 Suggest why
  a birds fluff out their feathers on a cold day
  b you should 'fluff up' a sleeping bag before using it
  c mountaineers who are lost in blizzards dig snow-holes for warmth.
7 Thought experiment: plan an investigation to find out which material will keep a container of water warm for the longest time.
8 **Try to find out** how Arctic animals survive in the winter.

The Blacks, the Browns, the Greens, and the Whites had two things in common. They lived in the same type of house, and had huge heating bills.

One year, they each had heating bills of nearly £2000. That made them think!

They decided that they would have to do something to reduce these bills. And so they decided to insulate their homes to cut down the amount of heat energy which was escaping.

Each family used a different kind of insulation.

Insulating walls with foam

The Blacks put insulation in the loft. They laid shiny aluminium foil above the ceiling, then covered it with glass-fibre wool 15 cm thick. They added foam lagging to exposed water pipes. It cost them £400 to do this. Their heating bills went down by £200 each year.

The Greens fitted double-glazed windows everywhere. These windows have two panes of glass with a layer of air trapped between them. This cost them £5000. Their bills went down by £200 each year. The house was quieter, too.

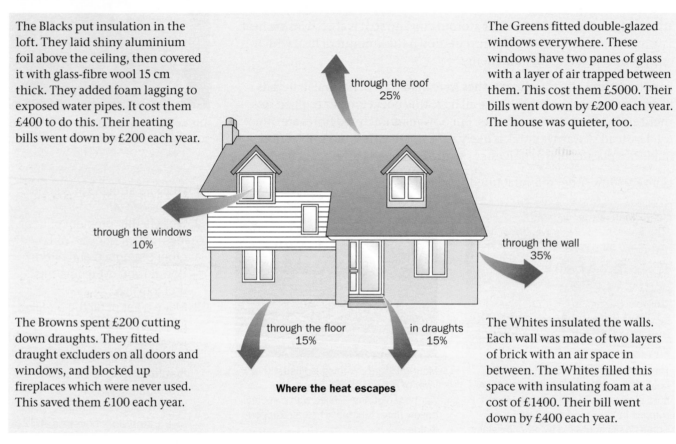

through the roof
25%

through the windows
10%

through the wall
35%

through the floor
15%

in draughts
15%

Where the heat escapes

The Browns spent £200 cutting down draughts. They fitted draught excluders on all doors and windows, and blocked up fireplaces which were never used. This saved them £100 each year.

The Whites insulated the walls. Each wall was made of two layers of brick with an air space in between. The Whites filled this space with insulating foam at a cost of £1400. Their bill went down by £400 each year.

1 List
  a *four* ways in which heat can escape from a house ▲
  b *four* ways of preventing heat from escaping.
2 Which methods of insulation use trapped air as an insulator?
3 Why is aluminium foil fixed above ceilings?
4 Explain how heat can escape through an unused fireplace.

5 How much did the Blacks
  a pay for insulation?
  b save each year? ▲
6 a The Blacks only really began to save money after two years. Explain this.
  b How many years passed before the other families began to save?
7 If you had to insulate a house, which two methods would you use first, and why?

DID YOU KNOW?
➲ One experimental house in Wales is so well insulated that its 17 rooms can be heated using only a 3-kilowatt heater. (This heater produces heat at the same rate as a three-bar electric fire.)

In a time of energy shortage, you aren't likely to be impressed by a home which loses 99.9% of the heat supplied to it. And yet your home – the Earth – does just that. Every day, a huge quantity of heat energy reaches the Earth from the Sun. Much of this heat is absorbed, warming up the land and the sea, but then, at night, practically all of the absorbed heat is lost again. It escapes into space as radiation while the Earth cools down.

With so much free energy being wasted, it's not surprising that scientists are trying to find ways of using and storing large quantities of **solar heat**. A number of methods of trapping this heat have been developed, but most of them suffer from one main disadvantage. The equipment used is expensive, which makes the large-scale use of solar heat a costly business.

Despite this, solar energy is used for heating homes and other larger buildings in many parts of the world. Even in Britain, where sunshine can hardly be guaranteed, solar heating is being used in many homes. The homes which use solar heating best are those which have been specially designed for that use. They have been built with

A solar cooker. It reflects the Sun's rays on to the pan.

one side facing south so that it receives sunshine most of the day.

large windows facing south. The Sun's heat rays travel through the glass and are absorbed inside the home.

a large greenhouse on the south side. The air in the greenhouse heats up. It can then be circulated through the house.

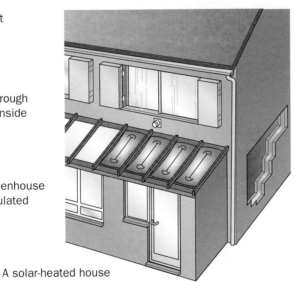

A solar-heated house

solar panels on the roof. Water from the house's hot water system trickles through the panels. As it does so, the Sun heats it up.

masses of **loft insulation.**

shutters on the windows to prevent heat from escaping when the air outside cools.

very thick walls which warm up during the day and radiate some of the heat into the house at night.

---

1 Why does the Earth's temperature
 a rise during the day and fall at night? ▲
 b change more on clear days (and nights) than on cloudy ones?
2 a Why is so little use made of solar energy? ▲
 b Suggest two reasons why Japan, the USA, and Israel have more solar-heated homes than any other country.

3 Why does the solar-heated house
 a face north and south?
 b have thick walls?
 c have shuttered windows?
 d have solar panels? ▲
4 a What colour should solar panels be, and why?
 b In what direction should solar panels point, and why?
5 Try to find out one other way of using solar energy.

DID YOU KNOW?

➲ The solar energy reaching the Earth in 1 year is more than 10 000 times greater than the world's energy needs.

➲ Solar panels can absorb useful amounts of heat even on cloudy days.

This is a salmon farm in the Western Isles. The environment for the hatching salmon is to some extent controlled by humans using the cages at centre. The salmon are fed with carefully designed food, to ensure that the energy introduced into the system is as efficiently used as possible. However, all around the farm, of course, is the natural environment. What effects does this have on the salmon farm, and what effects does the salmon farm have on the wider environment? In this chapter, you will learn more generally about how energy is taken from the environment and used by living things, both animals and plants.

Where does your body get its energy from?

1 **Your body has to get energy from somewhere**. It uses up energy all the time. Your body uses up energy:
- ⊃ when it grows
- ⊃ when your muscles move
- ⊃ to keep you warm.

2 **Your body gets the energy it needs from food.** There are large amounts of chemical energy stored in energy-rich foods like bread, cakes, cornflakes, crisps, chips, and sweets. You can make use of this energy by eating these foods. Your body changes the chemical energy to the kinds of energy it needs, like heat energy and moving energy.

Foods for energy

3 **The energy in food comes from the Sun!** Green plants use sunlight to make food from carbon dioxide and water. The process is called **photosynthesis**.

Many plants build up stores of chemical energy which can then be used to make your food. Wheat grains, for example, are stores of chemical energy built up by the wheat plant. Wheat grains are used to make flour for baking bread and cakes.

These three facts point to one thing:

the Sun is your body's energy source.

The energy you use on a wet winter run comes from summer sunshine!

light energy

5 miles later – still going strong

1 Why must your body be supplied with energy? ▲
2 Your body is an energy changer. Write down
  a the kind of energy it uses up
  b two kinds of energy it produces. ▲
3 Which energy change is carried out by green plants? ▲
4 Make a list of energy-rich foods you have eaten today.
5 Explain why 'the energy you use on a wet winter run comes from summer sunshine'.

DID YOU KNOW?

- ⊃ There is enough energy stored in one large slice of toast to keep a cross-country runner going for about 10 minutes.
- ⊃ Plants use less than 1/100th of the Sun's energy which reaches Earth.

Plants and their food

Many of the foods built up by plants are high-energy foods called **carbohydrates**. Glucose, sugar and starch, are three of these carbohydrates.

Plants store carbohydrates in different ways. These energy stores are important to the plants. The plants use them when they need energy. Plant energy stores are important to you too.

These peas are seeds which store sugar.

These carrots are roots where starch is stored.

Leaves like the ones on this cabbage have lots of starch.

Testing a leaf for starch

An easy way of finding out whether a plant is photosynthesizing is to see if its leaves have stored any starch.

Remember to wear safety glasses if you try this experiment.

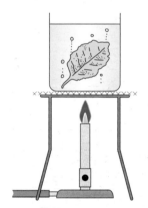

1 Put it in boiling water.

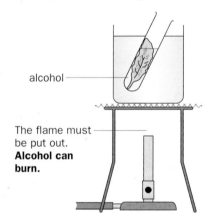

alcohol

The flame must be put out. **Alcohol can burn.**

2 Heat it in alcohol (to take away its green colour).

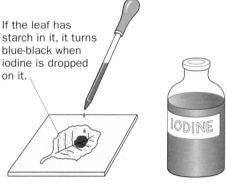

If the leaf has starch in it, it turns blue-black when iodine is dropped on it.

IODINE

3 Soften it in boiling water, then add iodine to it.

1 a What are carbohydrates?
  b Name two examples of carbohydrates. ▲
2 Why are energy stores important to plants? ▲
3 Name two foods that contain
  a sugar   **b** starch.
4 a What colour is iodine?
  b What colour does iodine go when it is mixed with starch? ▲
5 During the starch test:

  a Why is the leaf boiled in water for a while?
  b What is the job of the alcohol? ▲
6 Explain how the starch test can show whether or not a plant has been photosynthesizing.
  a Describe one important safety precaution that must be taken when doing the starch test.
  b Explain why this is important.

Food factories

Leaves are the 'food factories' of plants. They are where photosynthesis happens.

Leaves are well suited to their job.

- ⟳ They have lots of chlorophyll in their cells to absorb light.
- ⟳ They are broad and flat to absorb lots of light.
- ⟳ They have holes underneath to let gases in and out.
- ⟳ They have lots of veins to carry water to the photosynthesizing cells.

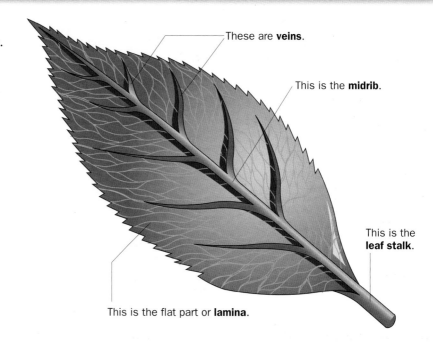

These are **veins**.

This is the **midrib**.

This is the **leaf stalk**.

This is the flat part or **lamina**.

Making food in leaves

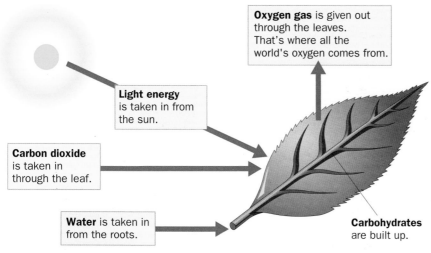

Oxygen gas is given out through the leaves. That's where all the world's oxygen comes from.

Light energy is taken in from the sun.

Carbon dioxide is taken in through the leaf.

Water is taken in from the roots.

Carbohydrates are built up.

oxygen

bubbles

pondweed

You can show that oxygen is produced during photosynthesis by using this apparatus.

1 Why are leaves able to
  a absorb lots of light?
  b get gases in and out?
  c get water to photosynthesizing cells? ▲
2 **a** Where does the energy for photosynthesis come from?
  b What green chemical absorbs this energy? ▲
3 **a** What two simple chemicals are needed for photosynthesis?

b How do these chemicals get into the leaf? ▲
4 What happens to the oxygen produced in photosynthesis? ▲
5 Suggest why these plants will not photosynthesize
  a a plant growing in the dark
  b a plant growing in air with no carbon dioxide in it
  c a plant with no water supply.
6 **Try to find out** why the cells on the surface of a leaf are transparent.

DID YOU KNOW?

- ⟳ Leaves don't breathe! Gases pass in and out by diffusion.
- ⟳ Green plants grow better in air which has extra carbon dioxide in it.

117

Limiting factors

Photosynthesis doesn't happen at the same rate all the time. Three things, called **factors**, can change the rate of photosynthesis in a plant. These are:

1 How much light there is

Chlorophyll uses light energy for photosynthesis. The more light energy there is, the faster photosynthesis will be. Even the colour of light is important. Plants photosynthesize best in red and blue light. Green light isn't used at all: it is reflected – that's why leaves are green.

These plants are growing in red light.

2 How much carbon dioxide there is

Carbon dioxide and water are the raw materials for photosynthesis. Without them a plant won't be able to make any food. There is usually lots of water available. But there isn't much carbon dioxide in the air (about 0.03%). More carbon dioxide means that photosynthesis can speed up and a plant will make more food.

Carbon dioxide is being added to the air in this greenhouse.

3 How hot or how cold it is

Photosynthesis is a chemical reaction. This reaction works best when it is warm. This is why the rate of photosynthesis is higher on warm days than on cold days. There is a problem, though. If it gets too hot, the chemical reaction stops altogether and there is no photosynthesis.

Plants make lots of food on warm, sunny days.

The best conditions

For a plant to have the best rate of photosynthesis, it needs
- enough light
- enough carbon dioxide
- a perfect temperature.

If one of these factors isn't right for some reason, photosynthesis will slow down. The factor that isn't right is called the **limiting factor**.

Light is a limiting factor in a wood. Ivy grows up tree trunks to get to the light.

1 Name three things that affect the rate of photosynthesis. ▲
2 Why are leaves green? ▲
3 Explain why photosynthesis will stop if a plant gets too hot. ▲
4 Describe the best conditions for photosynthesis.
5 What is a limiting factor?
6 **Try to find out** why bluebells flower early in the year.

DID YOU KNOW?

- Most plants photosynthesize best at about 25 °C.
- If a plant hasn't got enough chlorophyll, then this also becomes a limiting factor.

1 Animals use food to get the energy they need. They use oxygen and produce carbon dioxide, all the time.

2 Plants also use food to get the energy they need. They also use oxygen and produce carbon dioxide, all the time.

3 But during the day, green plants build up food! To do this, they use up carbon dioxide and produce oxygen. Overall, green plants produce more oxygen than they use.

In this way, oxygen and carbon dioxide are constantly being taken from, and added to, the atmosphere.

Up till about 200 years ago, the amounts of oxygen and carbon dioxide in the atmosphere stayed roughly the same. The green plants used up all the carbon dioxide produced by the animals. The green plants produced all the oxygen that the animals needed.

But since then, the amounts of oxygen and carbon dioxide in the atmosphere have been changing. There are two main reasons for this.

1 **More and more fuels are being burned.** In 1980, the amount of fuel burned was four times the amount burned in 1950. Burning huge quantities of fuel uses up lots of oxygen. It produces lots of carbon dioxide too.
2 **More and more trees are being cut down.** As many as $\frac{1}{50}$ of the world's trees may be cut down in a year. And so there are fewer trees to use up the carbon dioxide and to produce oxygen.

For these reasons, the amount of oxygen in the atmosphere is falling. But this isn't a serious worry. The world won't run out of oxygen. The slight increase in carbon dioxide, however, could cause problems. Carbon dioxide prevents heat escaping from the Earth. If there is extra carbon dioxide in the atmosphere, the world may gradually warm up. This may change the weather. It could even melt the ice at the Poles.

You **use up** the same amount of oxygen as that **made** by a large tree.

DiD YOU KNOW?

➲ Trees are the plants which use most carbon dioxide and produce most oxygen.

➲ The oxygen produced by the grass on a football pitch is used up by 75 fans in a 90-minute match.

➲ It needs a forest the size of Lothian to supply enough oxygen to burn the coal or oil used by one power station.

1 Write down three ways in which oxygen is taken from the atmosphere. ▲
2 Why did the amounts of oxygen and carbon dioxide in the atmosphere stay 'in balance' before 1800? ▲
3 Brazilian farmers clear land for farming by cutting down trees and burning them. How does this change the gases in the atmosphere?
4 Tests show that at night, a plant takes in oxygen and gets rid of carbon dioxide. On a sunny day, it takes in carbon dioxide and gets rid of oxygen. Explain what is happening.
5 **Try to find out** about the work of the Forestry Commission.

Food chains

Green plants build up their own food. They are called **producers**.

Animals can't build up their own food. They are called **consumers** ('to consume' means 'to eat'). **Primary consumers** are animals which live only on green plants. **Secondary consumers** are animals which feed on other animals. Secondary consumers are **predators**. The animals they eat are their **prey**.

A lettuce plant is a producer; a rabbit is a primary consumer; a fox is a secondary consumer. Lettuce makes its own food; rabbits eat lettuce; foxes eat rabbits. This makes up a **food chain**:

lettuce ──────→ rabbit ──────→ fox   (arrows mean 'is eaten by')

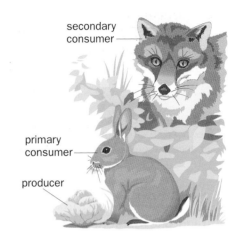

Food webs

But rabbits don't just eat lettuces. And foxes don't just eat rabbits. One food chain can only tell you a little about what different animals eat. **Food webs**, made up of a number of food chains, tell you more:

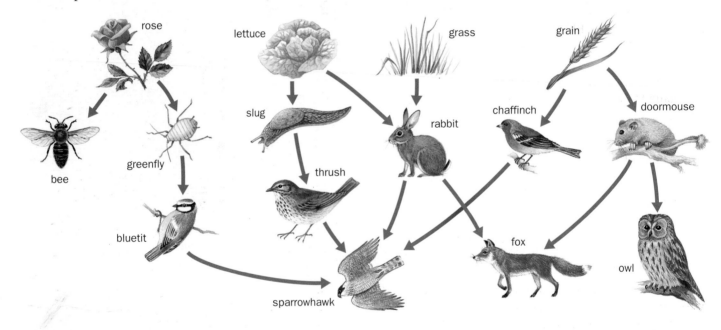

1 What is
   a a producer?
   b a primary consumer?
   c a secondary consumer? ▲
2 In the food chain
   lettuce → rabbit → fox
   what is
   a the predator?   **b** the prey?
3 About the food web:
   a Divide the animals and the plants into three sets –
   producers, primary consumers, and secondary consumers.
   b What does a sparrow hawk eat?
   c A sparrow hawk can help, and make difficulties for, a gardener. Explain why.
   d Does the dormouse move about mostly by day or night? Explain.
4 **Try to find out** which foods bees and greenfly get from roses What does a food chain show?

DiD YOU KNOW?
⮑ When food is scarce, a fox will eat berries.
⮑ Rabbits occasionally eat worms and snails.

Green plants don't just grow on land. The ocean has green plants, too. The most important of these are the *plant* plankton.

Plant plankton look very different from the plants you see every day. Plant plankton are microscopic. Most are made up of only one cell. But each of them contains chlorophyll. And so each tiny plant does the same job as a green plant on land. It uses sunlight to build up energy foods.

Plant plankton drift about in the sunlit waters near the surface of the sea. Other types of plankton live there, too. These are the slightly bigger *animal* plankton. Many of these animals are tiny shell fish which move about, feeding on the plant plankton.

Plant plankton

Animal plankton

Food chains in the sea

The largest amounts of plant plankton are found in shallower parts of the ocean, like the North Sea. That's why most fish are in these parts, too. But fish don't eat plant plankton. The tiny plants are too small for that. What happens is that:

...plant plankton are eaten by animal plankton...

...animal plankton are eaten by small fish...

...small fish are eaten by larger fish, which are eaten by larger fish, which are eaten by...

The sea's food chains can be long. Its food webs can be complicated. But they all start from plant plankton, the ocean's producers.

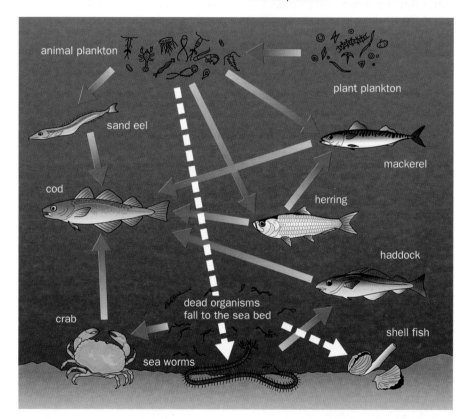

1 What are plant plankton like? Why are they called producers?
2 Write down some differences between animal and plant plankton.
3 Using the food web, write down
   a some foods eaten by mackerel
   b the fish which eat plankton
   c fish which feed on the bottom of the sea.
4 Why does the North Sea have large stocks of fish?
5 **Try to find out** what has happened to the cod stocks in the North Sea and why.

DID YOU KNOW?
➲ Sometimes parts of the North Sea have so much plankton that the water looks green.

➲ About 70% of the world's oxygen is produced by plant plankton.

For over 100 years, farmers have regarded the rabbit as a serious pest. It's not difficult to see why. Where rabbits are plentiful, plants suffer badly. The rabbits destroy all sorts of young plants by eating the new shoots. They also eat much grass which could be used for grazing sheep and cattle.

In 1953, large numbers of rabbits were deliberately wiped out by using a disease called myxomatosis. Soon after that, the countryside began to change. As you might expect, the most obvious change was in the plant life. More tree seedlings began to survive. Certain types of wild plant became more plentiful. Grasses which had been cropped short were able to grow to their full height. But the animal life changed, too. Some large plant-eating animals, like the hare and the deer, increased in numbers because there was more vegetation for them to feed on. Other meat-eating animals like the fox, the stoat, and the buzzard, which fed mainly on rabbits, became fewer in number. They had to look for other sources of food. That's why smaller animals, like mice and voles, began to suffer, too.

All this should help you to understand an important point about food webs:

Anything which affects one part of a food web affects other parts, too.

Sometimes, a change can have rather unexpected effects. You can see this in the following examples:
- In Poland, otters were killed to protect fish stocks. In fact, fish stocks fell.
- DDT, a pesticide, was sprayed onto apple trees to kill pests, including the red spider mite. But it didn't kill the mites. In fact, they multiplied.
- DDT was sprayed on to fields to kill insect pests. Later, heron, grebes, and other fish-eating birds were poisoned by the chemical.

Why did these things happen?

That's for you to work out in the questions.

Pretty to look at, but a pest to the farmer

When DDT was first used in Britain, the hawk population fell. Now the use of DDT is strictly controlled.

1 Why is the rabbit regarded as a pest? ▲
2 Why did the myxomatosis outbreak affect the numbers of:
   a buzzards?
   b deer?
   c mice? ▲
3 Explain how the unexpected effects mentioned above came about. Here are some clues:
   - otters often feed off diseased fish which are easy to catch;
   - red spider mites are preyed on by other small animals which live in the bark of apple trees;
   - DDT stays in the body tissues of any animal which eats it.
4 **Try to find out** when the rabbit was introduced into Australia, and what effect it had.

DID YOU KNOW?
- A female rabbit may have six or more litters in one year. She will produce between 3 and 8 young in each litter.
- In 1930, there were thought to be more than 100 000 000 rabbits in Britain.

Animals and plants live most of the time in a place that suits them best. This is called their **habitat**. You are more likely to find a particular animal or plant in one kind of habitat rather than in another. This is because their bodies are better adapted to some conditions than to others.

A woodland habitat

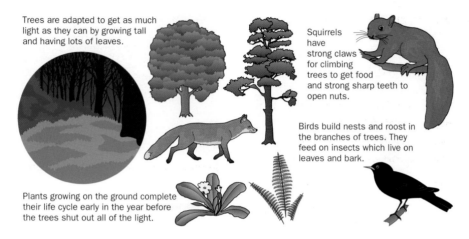

Trees are adapted to get as much light as they can by growing tall and having lots of leaves.

Squirrels have strong claws for climbing trees to get food and strong sharp teeth to open nuts.

Birds build nests and roost in the branches of trees. They feed on insects which live on leaves and bark.

Plants growing on the ground complete their life cycle early in the year before the trees shut out all of the light.

A river habitat

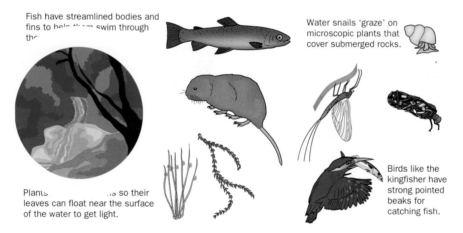

Fish have streamlined bodies and fins to help them swim through the...

Water snails 'graze' on microscopic plants that cover submerged rocks.

Plants ... ...s so their leaves can float near the surface of the water to get light.

Birds like the kingfisher have strong pointed beaks for catching fish.

A seashore habitat

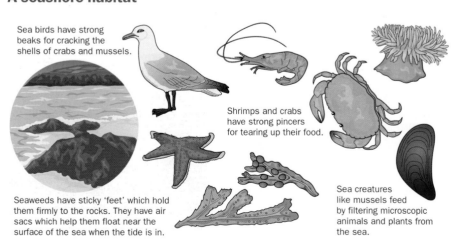

Sea birds have strong beaks for cracking the shells of crabs and mussels.

Shrimps and crabs have strong pincers for tearing up their food.

Seaweeds have sticky 'feet' which hold them firmly to the rocks. They have air sacs which help them float near the surface of the sea when the tide is in.

Sea creatures like mussels feed by filtering microscopic animals and plants from the sea.

1 **a** What is a habitat?
   b Why do you usually find animals and plants in only one kind of habitat? ▲
2 Primroses live on woodland floors. Explain how primroses are adapted to live in a woodland habitat ▲
3 What do woodland birds feed on? ▲
4 Why do river plants have long stems? ▲
5 How are fish adapted to their habitat? ▲
6 Describe the problems that seaweeds have to cope with in a seashore habitat.
7 **Try to find out** the names of two fish that can live in both a freshwater river and a sea habitat.

In any habitat there are always more living things born than can ever survive. Only the best suited to their habitat will survive. Competition happens between animals and plants of the *same* species and animals and plants of *different* species.

What do plants compete for?

Plants make their own food using light energy from the Sun. They must therefore get as much light as they can so that they can make as much food as possible. The plants that grow fastest and tallest usually survive.

Plants need water and minerals from the soil. They can't make food without them. Plants with roots that spread wider and deeper in the soil will be more likely to win the competition.

Bright, sweet-smelling flowers attract insects for pollination. The more attractive a flower is to insects, the better its chances of reproducing.

What do animals compete for?

If they are to survive, animals need food and water. Animals can move from place to place to get water.

The better an animal can avoid being seen by predators, the greater the chances of survival.

For the survival of the species, individual animals must mate. The bigger, fitter males usually win the battle to mate with the females.

---

1 List three things that
   a plants **b** animals
   compete for. ▲
2 Explain why successful plants
   have large root systems.
3 Explain why there are so many
   different kinds of attractive,
   sweetly scented flowers?

4 Explain how the zebra is
   adapted for survival.
5 Give one example of
   competition between
   a animals of the same species
   b animals of different species.
6 **Try to find out** why animals
   migrate.

DiD YOU KNOW?

➲ The Equador tree frog hides
   from predators by mimicking a
   pile of bird droppings!
➲ Chuckwalla lizards escape
   danger by crawling into cracks
   in rocks the inflating their
   bodies with air. This wedges
   them in so predators can't pull
   them out.

Pyramid of numbers

In most habitats there are many more producers than consumers, and more predators than prey.

In this food chain...

grass ——→ rabbit ——→ fox

...there are probably thousands and thousands of single grass plants, eaten by about 15 rabbits, which in turn may be eaten by one fox. As you move along the food chain, the number of living things in each 'link' gets a lot smaller. It takes a lot of food in one 'link' of the food chain to keep the animals in the next alive.

This information can be shown as a sort of bar chart. The length of each bar represents the numbers of living things in each link of the food chain.

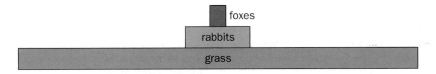

This is called a **pyramid of numbers**.

Not all pyramids are neat and tidy like the one shown above. Sometimes they look wrong.

Suppose the producer were a single oak tree. Feeding on the leaves could be thousands of caterpillars. Small birds feed on the caterpillars. In turn, thousands of fleas could be feeding on the blood they suck from the birds.

The 'pyramid' for this food chain is a very strange shape!

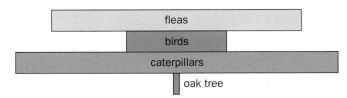

Pyramid of biomass

Biomass is a word used to describe the mass of living material in an area. If you could collect all of the plants and animals in an area and weigh them, this would be the biomass of that area.

So, if you draw a **pyramid of biomass** for the oak tree food chain, you get a true pyramid shape this time.

This is because the oak tree weighs a lot more than the animals in the rest of the food chain – even thousands of fleas!

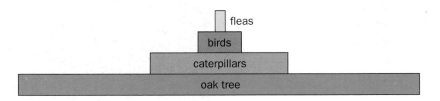

1 Why is the chart called a pyramid of numbers? ▲
2 What does the length of each bar stand for in a pyramid of numbers? ▲
3 Explain why pyramids of numbers can be different shapes.
4 Draw a pyramid of numbers for this information:
  a 1000 wheat plants, 20 field mice, 1 cat
  b 1 rose bush, 3000 greenfly, 1000 ladybirds, 2 blue tits.
5 a What is biomass?
  b Write down one food chain where the pyramids of numbers and biomass are
    i the same shape
    ii different shapes.
6 **Try to find out** the scientific name for each 'link' or level in a food chain.

Habitats are always changing, sometimes for better, sometimes for worse. There are a number of things that can cause a habitat to change. These can be divided into two main groups:

⊃ changes due to living things
⊃ changes due to non-living things.

The diagram below shows the sorts of things that can affect living things and their habitats:

Changes due to living things

1. Trees grow big and tall, stopping other plants getting light and water.
2. Animals eat more or fewer plants and other animals, affecting their numbers.
3. Humans take over the land for growing crops. They cut down trees and plough the soil.

Changes due to non-living things

1. A sudden temperature change can kill large numbers of animals and plants.
2. Severe storms and floods wash away the homes of burrowing animals like rabbits. Plants die if they are covered with water for long periods.
3. Forest fires destroy not only large numbers of plants but also the animals that depend on them for food.

1. What two things can affect where living things live? ▲
2. How do trees affect habitats? ▲
3. What affect can humans have on a natural habitat? ▲
4. Describe some of the effects that climate change could have on a habitat.
5. Explain why animals die as a result of forest fires.
6. **Try to find out** more about intensive fish farming.

DID YOU KNOW?

⊃ Clay soils hold more water but less air than sandy soils. Loam is a mixture of the two and gives the best of both worlds. More plants and more varieties of plants grow in loam soils than in either clay or sandy soils. Remember, plants like moist soil with lots of air spaces!